THE
MYTHIC
BESTIARY

THE MYTHIC BESTIARY

The Illustrated Guide to the World's Most Fantastical Creatures

Tony Allan

DUNCAN BAIRD PUBLISHERS

LONDON

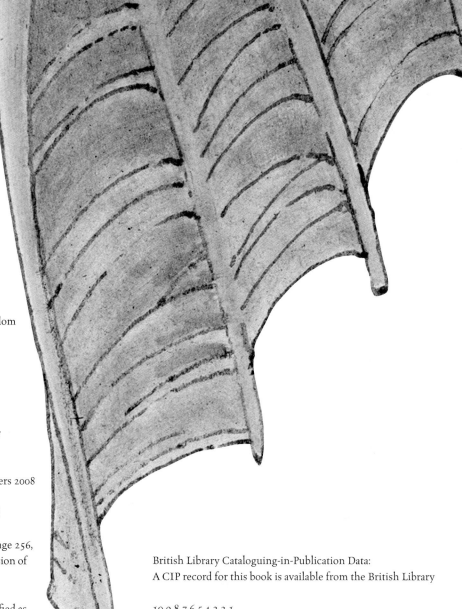

The Mythic Bestiary
Tony Allan

First published in the United Kingdom
and Ireland in 2008
by Duncan Baird Publishers Ltd
Sixth Floor, Castle House
75–76 Wells Street
London W1T 3QH

Conceived, created and designed by
Duncan Baird Publishers

Editor: James Hodgson
Designer: Gail Jones
Picture Research: Gillian Glasson
Managing Editor: Christopher Westhorp
Managing Designer: Daniel Sturges
Commissioning Designer: Paul Reid at Cobalt id
Commissioned artworks: Tomislav Tomic, Peter Visscher
   and Garry Walton

British Library Cataloguing-in-Publication Data:
A CIP record for this book is available from the British Library

10 9 8 7 6 5 4 3 2 1

ISBN: 978-1-84483-458-7

Typeset in Celestia Antiqua
Colour reproduction by Scanhouse, Malaysia
Printed in Singapore by TWP

NOTES
Abbreviations used throughout this book:
BCE Before the Common Era (the equivalent of BC)
CE Common Era (the equivalent of AD)

Contents

Part 2:
Beasts of the Earth 54

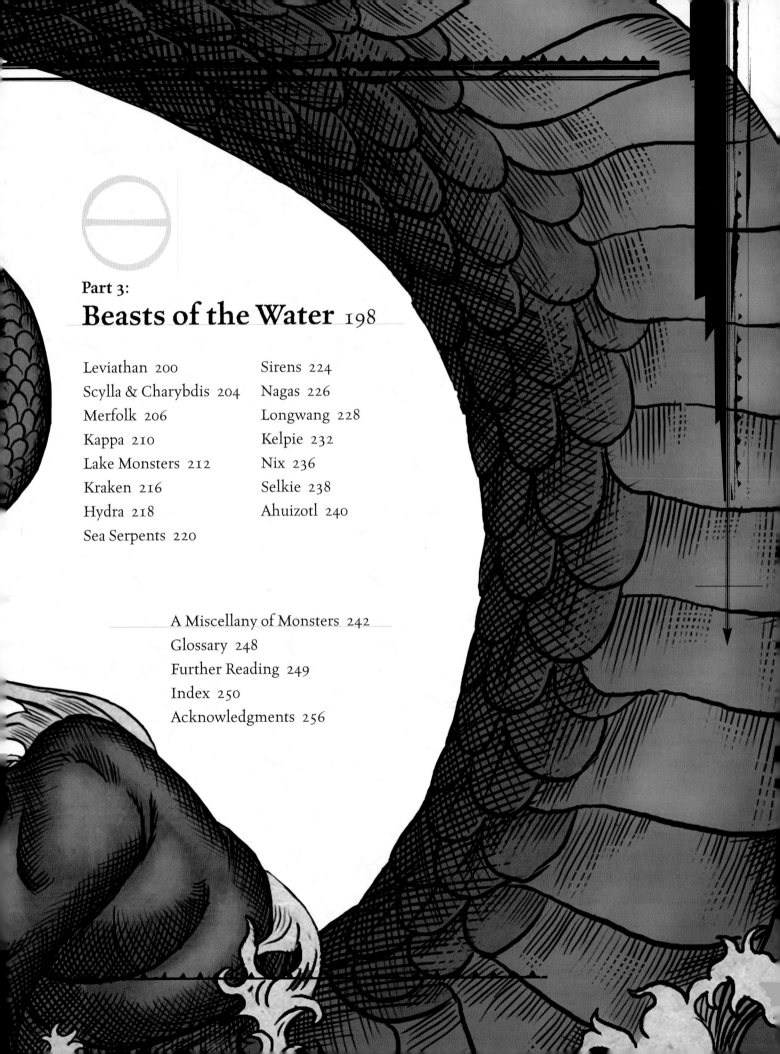

Part 3:
Beasts of the Water 198

Introduction

Mythical beasts are creatures of the human imagination. They make up a strange fauna, shaped from our hopes and aspirations but much more from our deepest fears. They are the wildlife of the unconscious, a zoo peopled by the shadow-creatures that haunt our dreams.

By and large, the animals described here are not the creations of any single, known author. Fictional creatures are not included unless they have somehow made the leap into a wider sphere of recognition. So there are no jabberwocks or pobbles, and none of the multifarious beings that creep, crawl, slither or teleport themselves through science-fiction novels and films. J.R.R. Tolkien's orcs do put in an appearance, though, because they seem to be acquiring a life beyond his works. The same is even more true of gnomes. Originally the invention of the extraordinary healer and polymath Paracelsus, they now proudly adorn gardens across the Western world.

> "Mythical animals tend to fall into certain natural types or categories, the phyla, orders and genera of the imagination's zoo."

Mythical animals tend to fall into certain natural types or categories, the phyla, orders and genera of the imagination's zoo. Before examining these classifications more closely, it is perhaps worth noting that all imagined beings are not equal. Some, like dragons or giants, seem to be almost universal in their relevance, cropping up in the mythologies of many nations. Others, like the mermecolion or the chimera, are improbable and hard to visualize and have only a limited diffusion; they are, as it were, chimerical.

For the most part, though, the inhabitants of the mythical bestiary are deeply grounded in the imaginative landscape, and many trace their origins back to the most ancient times. Part of the parentage of dragons springs from primeval serpent beings, and they in turn can be tracked back to the Mesopotamian creation myth known as the *Enuma Elish*. It tells how the creator god Marduk killed Tiamat, the primordial

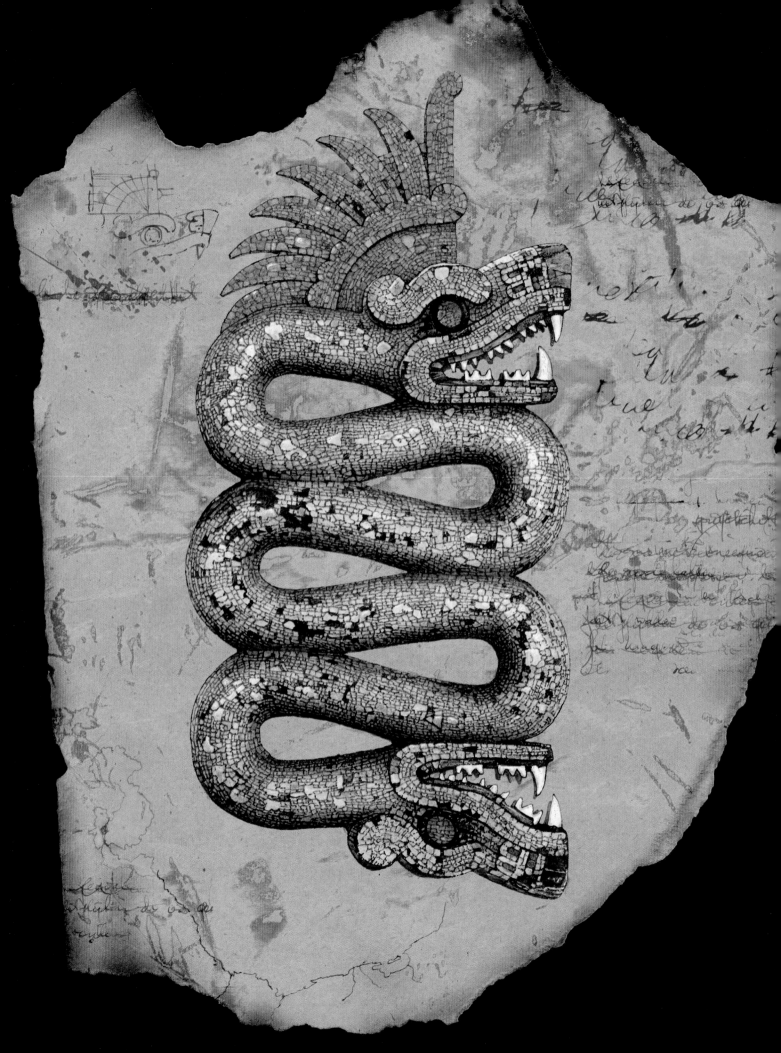

> "India's nagas and China's long-wang dragon kings were regal beings who lorded it over the seas and inland waters."

serpent goddess of the sea, and split her body in two to create the heavens and Earth. Ancient Egypt had a cosmic serpent in the form of Apep, who waited nightly just beyond the gates of dusk in the hope of swallowing up the Sun god Ra and so removing light from the Earth. Far away across the Atlantic, Mesoamerican peoples quite independently dreamed up a snake god of their own in the feathered serpent Quetzalcoatl (see illustration, page 9), a culture hero for the Aztecs who helped create humankind in its present form and gave people maize and knowledge of weaving.

Stranger than the sum of their parts

The Mesoamericans endowed Quetzalcoatl with the plumage of the Resplendent quetzal, a gorgeous bird of the forest. They thereby created an example of one of the most characteristic forms of mythical beast – the hybrid. The mythical zoo is well stocked with creatures combining aspects of more than one species. Classical mythology was particularly rich in this respect, blending humans with horses, lions, goats, birds and bulls to create, respectively, centaurs, manticores, satyrs, sirens and the Minotaur. Then there were inter-animal matings, like griffins, which combined features of the lion and the eagle. Other parts of the world showed a similar taste for bringing together disparate body parts to create something new. Japanese legend, for example, had tengu birdmen and the bizarre water spirits known as kappas, which melded elements of monkeys, frogs and tortoises.

Classical myth also showed the way in devising a purpose for the hybrids it created. They served above all as challenges to test the mettle of heroes. Sometimes success lay in making an ally of the beast, as when Bellerophon, with the help of the goddess Athene, succeeded in taming Pegasus to help him achieve wonders. More often, though, the creature was an adversary. Hercules faced an entire menagerie of mutants, from the many-headed Lernean hydra to the brass-beaked, man-eating Stymphalian birds. In similar fashion Bellerophon himself vanquished the chimera, Theseus the Minotaur, and Perseus Medusa, the snake-haired Gorgon. Christian legend inherited the tradition, creating not just St George but a whole legion of intrepid dragon-slayers. Yet this trait too is found outside the West; the Japanese warrior Yorimitsu overcame gigantic spider creatures, while Russian folktales more gently sent handsome princes on quests to find the firebird and bring it back alive.

Mythical beasts also served as guardians. Shedu (see illustration, below) and lammasu, gigantic winged bulls and lions, stood at the entrances of Mesopotamian temples and palaces, keeping out evil spirits. India's nagas and China's longwang dragon kings were regal beings who lorded it over the seas and inland waters. In Norse myth, dragons protected treasure, most memorably in the form of Fafnir, killed by the hero Sigurd or Siegfried in his quest for the dwarf king's gold.

In certain cases the realm that the monsters tended was the kingdom of the dead. One of Hercules' foes, the triple-headed dog Cerberus, stood guard over the classical Underworld just as his Norse equivalent Garm did outside Niflheim, the dread abode of the death goddess Hel. In early classical times winged harpies flew with human souls to Pluto's realm, while in Indian myth the bird god Garuda (see illustration, page 13) flew to the netherworld of Patala to rescue his mother Vinata from the nagas.

11

The fauna of fear

A wholly different class of beings existed on the borderline of life and death, embodying people's terror of the grave and of those who might come back from it. Far from guarding the land of the dead, however, they intruded across its boundaries. Theirs was the world of the undead, of ghosts, ghouls, zombies and vampires, and they were generally creatures of horror, born of primal fears of extinction and the grim realities of bodily decay.

Other monstrous creations gave form to the dread that afflicted all humans, but especially children, in the face of the unseen dangers of the world

around them. These bugaboos and bogeymen were often associated with particular locations. The witch Baba Yaga haunted the gloomy fir-glades of old Russia, the Anglo-Saxon Grendel (see illustration, below) was a creature of the swamps and fens, while wendigos personified all the anxieties associated with the forests of North America.

Other basic emotions besides fear could be bodied forth in myth. There were beings, typically female, who symbolized the temptations of the flesh, like the Hebrew Lilith or the classical Lamia, half woman and half snake. German nix and Slav rusalki were beautiful water spirits who lured men to death by drowning. Another class of creature effectively represented power, inspiring not so much trepidation as awe. A favourite image in this respect was a giant bird: the Arabian roc, the Persian simurgh, the Native American thunderbird. Part lion and part eagle, griffins combined elements of the top predators of land and sky, playing a similar role for the classical world.

Yet of all the various types of being that the world's mythologies invented, the most numerous were probably the extraordinary people. Almost every culture had tales of giants. These could be benign, but, humans being the nervous beings they are, they more often took fearsome form as ogres. Even more diverse were the innumerable little peoples – dwarfs, elves, imps, goblins – that shared habitat with their human cousins. The relationship was sometimes very close indeed; boggarts, kobolds and other house spirits even shared families' homes. More interesting, perhaps, was the idea of an alternative society living alongside our own, as exemplified by the fairy folk of Irish myth. Existing in a timeless land without ageing or death, they represented a dreamy Otherworld that reflected but also mocked the human condition.

Transformations also accorded rich pickings for the mythmaker's imagination. Many traditions harboured tales of seemingly normal individuals who could unexpectedly change into entirely different species. There were werecats in world mythology as well as werewolves, and Japan made much of its kitsune, or werefoxes.

Monstrous monastic misinterpretation

Amid all the richness there was room too for simple misinformation – creatures born not of the imagination but from distorted recording or sheer misunderstanding of travellers' tales. Copied down by monks in remote monasteries, the medieval bestiaries were full of bizarre animals reported at second- or fifth- or a hundredth-hand, whose features may once have had some basis in truth but had become warped in the course of repeated retelling. To these chance malformations we owe such oddities as the basilisk with its fatal gaze, the dog-headed Cynocephali, the blemmyes whose faces were in their chests, the one-legged sciapods, the bonnacon with its fiery dung and the amphisbaena, a snake with a head at each end.

The conundra of cryptozoology

Any smugness modern readers might feel about such eccentricities are easily dispelled by considering the limitations of our own knowledge. Few people suspected that the coelacanth, a Cretaceous Era survivor, still existed until one was fished live from the sea in 1938. Controversy still surrounds such creatures, long claimed as real, as sea serpents and lake monsters and the various types of apemen, from yetis and sasquatches to almas and *orang mawas*.

Urban legend has even added new candidates like the US Mothman and the chupacabras of Puerto Rico and neighbouring lands. Such beasts are the domain of the semi-science of cryptozoology.

One type of mythical creature is exceptional in seeming to be largely limited to a single cultural tradition. That is the propitious beast, whose appearance in China denotes an age of wisdom and good governance. One such is the qilin, or Chinese unicorn, another the fenghuang or Chinese phoenix. In a fantastic world dominated by monsters, such benign beings deserve to be better known. So let us begin the tour with a modern bestiarist's blessing: May a qilin someday grace your garden and a fenghuang alight on your roof.

13

Part I
Beasts of the Air

⊙ ⊕ ⊖

Thunderbird Awesome storm-bringer

Appearance
Huge, eagle-like bird with feathered horns and a down-turned beak.

Size
Large enough to carry a whale in its talons.

Lifespan
An elemental force, and so presumably eternal.

Powers
Created thunder by the beating of its wings and lightning by opening and closing its eyes.

Habitat
Craggy mountain peaks in North America, from the northwest Pacific coast to the Eastern Woodlands. Also reported as far south as California.

Hearing a clap of thunder or seeing a flash of lightning in the sky, Native Americans would look up in awe, for they knew that the mighty thunderbird was passing. The bird personified thunder for tribes across the continent. Algonquian-speaking peoples spoke of the thunderbirds as "our grandfathers", ancestral spirit forebears whose help could be sought in prayers. The Sioux called them *Wakinyan* and swore by them over the sacred pipe; anyone who subsequently lied could expect to be struck down by lightning.

For nobody ever doubted the thunderbirds' terrible power. The Ojibwa of the Great Lakes region told of two rash youths who decided to explore a mountain peak where the birds were said to live. Without performing any of the necessary rites, the two set off on their climb. The summit was shrouded in mist, but the more foolhardy of the two pressed on. His friend heard him shout: "I see them! I see them!" as he disappeared into the cloud. Then there was a terrible crash and a blinding flash of light. As the friend staggered backward, he saw the lifeless body of his companion tumbling down the mountainside.

For those who treated them with respect, however, the thunderbirds could be valuable helpers. The Makah people of the Northwest Coast had a story of a thunderbird that saved a village from famine by snatching a whale from the ocean and delivering it to the community, which fed off its flesh for many weeks. In the Eastern Woodlands, where fire and drought were serious threats, the thunderbird was venerated for its association with rain. Some Iroquois tribes called the bird *Oskadagea* or "dew eagle", claiming it carried the dew in a great depression on its back. In times of drought it could release its burden.

The Lakota Sioux told of a great battle that set the birds against the *untekhi*, evil water creatures committed to the destruction of the human race. Seeing humankind in danger, the thunderbirds flocked to their defence. They released all their thunderbolts at once in a climactic volley. The *untekhi* were shrivelled in the flames. But the humans survived on the high rock where they had taken refuge. To this day their descendants still point out the bones of the *untekhi*, turned to rock in the barren Badlands where the conflict raged.

Pegasus Winged horse of classical legend

Appearance
Winged horse.

Size
Equine.

Lifespan
After flying to Mt. Olympus, the home of the gods, Pegasus was transformed by Zeus into the constellation that bears his name.

Powers
Mastery of flight.

Habitat
Ancient Greece, where the hero Bellerophon found the horse grazing on the acropolis of Corinth.

The winged horse of Greek myth had an unseemly gestation. Sired by Poseidon, god of horses as well as of the sea, on the Gorgon Medusa, Pegasus was born when the hero Perseus sliced off Medusa's head, being generated from her blood as soon as it hit the ground.

Subsequently he became associated with streams. The poet Hesiod linked his name with *pege*, Greek for "spring". According to legend, the Hippocrene spring on Mount Helicon, sacred to the Muses, first sprang forth where Pegasus stamped the earth with his hoof.

Pegasus was tamed by Athene. When the hero Bellerophon needed a mount to confront the dreaded Chimera (see pages 108–109), he made offerings to the goddess, who provided him with a golden bridle to throw over the horse's head. He found Pegasus drinking from the spring of Pirene on the slopes of the acropolis at Corinth. Having brought him under control with the aid of Athene's magical gift, he was able to launch an aerial assault on the Chimera, shooting it down with arrows fired from on high.

Bellerophon was to complete other heroic deeds from Pegasus's back, but eventually his ambition overreached itself. He tried to fly to the summit of Mount Olympus itself, as though he were already an immortal. Zeus punished him by sending a gadfly to sting the horse, which threw its rider, sending him plunging down to earth. Pegasus himself continued to the home of the gods, where he was welcomed and given a new job drawing Zeus's thunder-chariot. Later legends claimed that he stayed there until the day of his death, when he was transformed for his services into the constellation of stars that still bears his name.

BURAQ, THE HEAVENLY STEED

In Islamic tradition the Prophet Muhammad was transported by a being called Buraq from Mecca to Jerusalem and then on to the seventh heaven all in a single night. Originally an angel, Buraq – the name means "lightning" – later came to be thought of as a heavenly steed, "larger than a donkey but smaller than a mule", which could reach the horizon in a single stride. Buraq was usually portrayed as a milk-white horse with a man's face and the wings of an eagle – or, among Muslims in India, with a peacock's wings and tail.

Strix The owl's inauspicious alter ego

Appearance
Vampiric night creatures that either sucked the blood or rent the flesh of human victims, usually identified as owls (*strix* being classical Greek for "owl").

Size
The Eagle owls known to the Romans would have had wingspans of up to 6ft (almost 2m).

Lifespan
Unknown. Real-life owls typically live for 6–8 years, although some have been known to reach the age of 15.

Powers
Supernatural predators capable of taking on and killing human prey. All owls were regarded as birds of ill omen, whose appearance might presage death.

Habitat
Waste places and ruins.

Anyone who has seen a barn owl hunting in the twilight, its great wings white against the shadows, knows how awesome the birds can be. People woken by the cry of a screech owl in the small hours have most likely shuddered at its eerie call. From such characteristics the Romans created the strix, a supernatural creature of the night that preyed on human flesh and foretold doom.

Stories of the strix were mostly vague and unspecific. Ovid spoke of them attacking the legendary King Procas in his cradle until they were warded off with sacrificial offerings. The Greeks told a tale of a woman called Polyphonte who mated with a bear, producing cannibalistic sons. Her punishment was to be transformed into a strix "that cries by night, a harbinger of war and civil strife". Seneca the Younger described the creatures as living on the edge of Tartarus.

To understand how the familiar owl was transformed into the sinister strix, it is best to trace the legends back to their roots in morphological fact. The owl order, its principal family still known as the Strigidae, is indeed nocturnal,

and more than half of all birds active at night belong to its ranks. Owls are consequently difficult to observe, and their habits are less well known than those of diurnal avians; even today, new species are still being discovered. The birds are perfectly adapted for hunting in the dark, equipped as they are with huge eyes for low-light vision and sharp beaks and talons curved for the kill. They are silent predators, their flight hushed by thousands of downy feathers. To avoid discovery, they tend to nest in desolate places and ruined buildings.

A bird to be dreaded

Small wonder, then, that the Romans, whose traditions of augury relied heavily on bird-watching, viewed them as singularly inauspicious. According to Pliny the Elder, the owl was "more to be dreaded than any other bird" in auspices connected with the state; when an owl once strayed into the Capitol, the building could not be reused until a full lustration (ritual cleansing) had been conducted. An owl spotted before Marcus Crassus's disastrous clash with the Parthians at

Carrhae in 53 BCE was thought to have presaged the Roman defeat.

Similar beliefs can be found in the Bible, where owls are associated with destruction; Isaiah said of one town targeted for divine wrath that "the owl and the raven shall dwell in it". Such images fed into the medieval bestiaries, in which the birds attracted additional odium for preferring the dark to the light, making them symbolic of sinfulness.

Some parallels with the Roman strix can be found in African folk belief. In Yoruba legend, witches and sorcerers could take the shape of owls at night and enter victims' houses to suck their blood. Some Ghanaian peoples believed that witches had owls as their familiars and sometimes shape-shifted with them on their nocturnal forays.

The strix's legacy also lived on in Rome's successor cultures. The creature gave its name to the Italian *strega* (witch) and to the Romanian *strigoi*, living dead who rose from the tomb to haunt the countryside at night in animal or spirit form. Elements of both traditions blended in the Albanian *shtriga*, night-hags who sucked the vital spirit out of people while they slept – then escaped by transforming themselves not into owls but rather flying insects.

Caladrius · Bird of healing with strange prognostic powers

Appearance
A bird of pure white plumage.

Size
Usually shown as gull-sized.

Lifespan
Not known.

Powers
Said to be able to cure jaundice, and to foretell whether a sick person would live or die. Its droppings could reputedly heal cataracts.

Habitat
Thought to live on the banks of rivers.

Little known now, a work that exerted a huge influence for over a thousand years first saw the light of day in Alexandria, Egypt, in the second century CE. It became known as the *Physiologus*, from its repeated use of the phrase "The *physiologus* (naturalist) says", and it was to be the model for all the medieval bestiaries. These works ostensibly took natural history as their theme, demonstrating the wonders of the creation in terms of the fauna that populated it. Written as they were in the high Age of Faith, however, they were at least as interested in conveying theological messages as in describing animal behaviour.

The bestiaries mostly drew on existing printed sources for their information rather than on direct observation of nature. So stories preserved in the *Physiologus* continued to crop up in later works throughout the Middle Ages, even though to modern eyes many of them seem far-fetched. One such myth was the notion that the pelican draws blood from its own breast to feed its young. There was no zoological justification for this story, which perhaps sprang from the bird's habit of resting its head on its chest, but it was nonetheless repeated up until modern times, when scientists finally took the trouble to study pelicans in their natural habitat. The legend owed its enduring popularity to its neat allegorical application as a metaphor for Christ, who gave up his own life for the sake of the human race.

A similar fate attended the caladrius, an otherwise unknown bird said to have pure white plumage and credited with prognostic powers. Introduced into a sickroom, it indicated by its behaviour what the outcome of the patient's condition was likely to be. To quote the *Physiologus*: "If the man is destined to die, it turns its face from him, and by this sign the people know that he is doomed.

> "Introduced into a sickroom, the caladrius indicated by its behaviour what the outcome of the patient's condition was likely to be."

If, on the other hand, the illness is not mortal, the caladrius looks into the face of the man, and as though it would draw the whole infirmity upon itself it flies toward the Sun, burning up the sickness and dispersing it in the open air, and so the patient is cured."

Like the pelican's act of self-sacrifice, the bird's curative powers pointed an obvious Christian moral. The caladrius too was symbolic of Christ, who took on himself the sins of humankind and carried them heavenward through his resurrection. The twelfth-century *Aberdeen Bestiary* spelled out the message: "Each day Christ, like the caladrius, attends us in our sickness, examines our mind when we confess, and heals those to whom he shows the grace of repentance. But he turns his face away from those whose heart he knows to be unrepentant. These he casts off; but those to whom he turns his face, he makes whole again."

Various attempts, none of them very convincing, have been made to identify the caladrius with particular avian species, from white parrots or doves to the White wagtail. A more likely link is with the Bird of Truth, able instinctively to identify murderers and other wrongdoers – a folktale motif found everywhere from Africa to the tales of the *1,001 Nights* and the Brothers Grimm.

Stories of the caladrius and its divinatory powers may also have contributed to the worldwide superstition linking birds and mortality. In many cultures a bird flying into a room was long considered an omen of approaching death. In England an enduring tradition claimed that two white birds appeared whenever a bishop of Salisbury was dying – a legend that was last evoked as recently as 1911.

Basilisk & Cockatrice Unnaturally born killers

Appearance
Varied. Pliny described the basilisk as a snake with a white, crown-shaped spot on its head. Medieval writers, however, visualized cockatrices as winged cockerels with serpent's tails.

Size
"Not more than a foot in length", according to Pliny. Medieval bestiaries credited cockatrices with longitudinal stripes 6 inches (15cm) wide.

Lifespan
Unspecified. The odour of weasels could kill basilisks.

Powers
A lethal gaze that killed all it fell upon. The creatures' bite and smell were also equally deadly.

Habitat
The desert of eastern Libya (Cyrenaica), according to Pliny.

Although conceived in very different ways, basilisk and cockatrice were two different takes on a single mythical beast whose overriding feature was its devastating lethal power. One glance from either could kill; indeed, the very smell of the creatures was fatal.

The basilisk was the original version. The name meant "little king" in Greek, and the beast itself was considered the king of serpents. As described by Pliny the Elder it was a snake less than a foot long with a white spot on its head in the shape of a crown. Its mere presence was enough to blast the earth around it, burning grass and splitting rocks.

Pliny also recorded that the only way to kill basilisks was to throw them into weasels' dens, for the odour was fatal to them. In Pliny's account the weasels also died, although medieval versions of the story had the tiny mammals actually killing the snakes.

By then, however, the basilisk itself had undergone a strange transformation. A story had spread that it was born, freakishly, from an egg laid by a cock. Some accounts added other, equally unlikely preconditions: Sirius had to be in the ascendant, and the egg had to be hatched by a toad. The offspring duly took on features of its sire. Chaucer called the result a basilicok in *The Canterbury Tales*, but the more normal name was "cockatrice".

The cockatrice inherited all the basilisk's lethality. Even birds flying overhead were said to be frizzled up and killed by its gaze. Yet it looked very different, for medieval illustrators chose to make it appear less like a snake than a cockerel with a serpent's tail. People had no doubt of its real existence, for the word had found its way into editions of the Bible.

By the Renaissance, sceptical voices started to be raised. The French jurist Jean Bodin asked rhetorically, "If the basilisk kills by merely being seen, then who has ever seen it?" Subsequently rationalists would argue that Pliny's account had in fact reflected garbled stories of king cobras, whose hoods became his crownlike markings. In this view, the creatures' true nemeses were not weasels but mongooses, unknown in Italy in Pliny's day but later renowned for their snake-slaying skills.

Garuda Divine birdman of Indian myth

Appearance
Half man, half raptor, with a golden body, white face and red wings.

Size
Large enough to block out the Sun.

Lifespan
According to the *Mahabharata*, granted immortality by Vishnu after he had carried off amrita, the drink of the gods.

Powers
Cosmic, as the aerial mount of the Hindu god Vishnu.

Habitat
A stone shrine in the form of a wheeled chariot forming part of the sacred complex at Vijayanagar was claimed to be his home. In Buddhist tradition, garudas inhabited groves of silk-cotton trees.

Like so much else in Indian myth, Garuda was a complex figure whose name meant different things to different people. Few, however, doubted his importance, for he played a central role in Hinduism as Vishnu's mount, carrying the great god through the air on his back. A Purana – Sanskrit sacred book – bore his name, as did one of the Upanishads (holy texts) of the Muktika canon.

Evidence suggests that Garuda was originally an archaic sun god, and was worshipped as such in temples. Legend maintained that he was born at the start of creation from the golden egg that also produced Brahma. In time, however, he became a hybrid figure, combining human and avian features, typically in the form of a man's face and body and a bird's beak and wings. As such, he was king of the aerial realm, and the beat of his mighty pinions was so powerful it could stop the rotation of the Earth.

The *Mahabharata* told a different tale. It made Garuda the son of the sage Kasyapa and his wife Vinata, and told of a heroic quest that he made to obtain amrita, the nectar of the gods, in order to free his mother from the clutches of the naga race of semi-divine serpents (see pages 226–227). His courage so impressed Vishnu that the god chose him as his own winged steed.

Buddhist tradition had yet another take on the story. In place of a single Garuda it spoke of garudas, huge birds that had much in common with the simurgh of Persian myth (see pages 30–31). The garudas were beings of great power; the flapping of their wings could stir up hurricanes and beat down houses. They were also intelligent and social, and they helped protect the holy mountain of Sumeru from the attacks of the asuras, demons who constantly threatened it.

One feature the garudas had in common with Garuda was a hatred of serpents, with whom they were held to be constantly at war. Snakes being regarded everywhere with suspicion, the enmity helped cement the birds' reputation as benefactors of humankind as well as lords of the sky – an enviable combination that caused the Indonesian government in recent times to choose Garuda as the name of the national airline.

Stymphalian Birds Man-eating marsh birds

Appearance
Man-eating birds with beaks, talons and wings of brass.

Size
The size of cranes.

Lifespan
Unspecified, but vulnerable to slingshots and arrows.

Powers
A taste for human flesh, plus the ability to shoot their feathers like arrows. In addition, their droppings were toxic.

Habitat
The shores of Lake Stymphalos in Arcadia, located in the northeast of Greece's Peloponnese peninsula.

In Alfred Hitchcock's 1963 thriller *The Birds*, inspired by a story by Daphne du Maurier, a seaside community is terrorized by predatory gulls that turn their aggression on humans. The film caused something of a sensation because of its unexpected plot. Most people had grown up thinking of birds as harmless creatures, giving the movie's premise real shock value.

In myth too, birds were normally treated favourably unless they were either hybrids or else magnified to enormous size. Even then, creatures like the roc, the simurgh and the thunderbird were viewed more with respect and awe than with outright terror.

So the Stymphalian birds of classical legend had few counterparts over the centuries. Sacred to the war god Ares (the Roman Mars), they acquired their evil reputation primarily from their habit of dining on human flesh. Then again, tradition credited them with metallic feathers along with brazen beaks and talons, thereby quashing the possibility that they might be regarded as soft, downy and lovable.

The story went that a vast flock of these avian predators had been driven northward by packs of wolves from their original roosting grounds near the city of Orchomene in Greece's Peloponnese peninsula. They settled instead in the marshes around Lake Stymphalos, located in the shadow of Mount Cyllene within the ancient province of Arcadia. There they spread devastation, stripping fruit trees for food and destroying crops with their toxic droppings. Farmers who tried to drive them away were struck down by a lethal rain of feathers, fired like arrows from the bird's wings. The men's corpses would be found half-eaten, the eyes pecked out and the soft parts consumed.

Such was the foe that Hercules confronted in his sixth labour. When he first approached the birds in their marshy lair, he found the terrain so boggy that he could not get close enough to rouse them from their nests. He turned for help to his divine backer Athene, who persuaded Hephaestus, god of metal-working, to provide the hero with a vast pair of bronze clappers (or, according to other sources, a bronze rattle). Equipped with this gigantic bird-scarer, he climbed onto a spur of Mount Cyllene and made such a din that all the birds took to the air as one in a single angry flock.

It was just the opportunity Hercules was waiting for. Taking up his bow, he fired off arrow after arrow, sending the birds crashing to a noisy death in the reeds below. (Again, other sources have him using a catapult or a sling to similar effect.) The survivors rose high above him in alarm and set off northward, never to be seen in Arcadia again. Hercules was able to leave the region purged of pests, secure in the knowledge of a job well done.

As for the birds, some people said that they flew to the Black Sea, taking refuge on an offshore islet known as the Isle of Ares. Jason and the Argonauts encountered them there while sailing for Colchis in search of the Golden Fleece. The flock circled above them, shooting metal plumes at the boat and wounding one man – Oileus, the father of Ajax – in the shoulder. The crew took defensive measures. Half raised their shields to form a protective umbrella, while the rest rowed the ship out of danger.

Over the centuries many scholars have speculated on the birds' origins,

seeking rational explanations behind the myths. Some suggested they may have originated as fever demons haunting the marshes, which were always considered unhealthy; people are known to have

used rattles and castanets in ancient times to scare such beings away. Others have proposed that the real Herculean labour lay in draining the marshes rather than ridding them of pests, using an underground channel that sometimes got blocked. One Athenian general, Iphicrates, is known to have considered deliberately obstructing this conduit while besieging a nearby city and was only dissuaded by a portent indicating that the gods opposed his plan.

29

⊙ ⊕ ⊖

Simurgh Persia's benevolent nurturer of heroes

30

Persian legend told a tale of a king whose first-born son was born with snow-white hair. Regarding the birth as an evil portent, the ruler ordered that the infant be taken to the Elburz Mountains in the northernmost region of Persia and left exposed to die. The abandoned child was found by the simurgh, largest and wisest of all the birds, and carried back to her nest on the highest peak, where she raised him as part of her own feathered brood.

The boy grew up tall and strong under her tender loving care. Meanwhile, the king remained childless, and as time passed he found himself thinking longingly of the son he had so cruelly cast away. When reports reached him of a sturdy albino youth seen roaming the fells, hope stirred in his breast. He went with a large retinue to the mountains to find out whether there was any truth to the stories, and there the simurgh delivered his long-lost son to him.

Yet the bird's benevolence did not end with the transfer. Before leaving the young man, who was subsequently named Zal, she told him (for she had the power of speech as well as wisdom) to take a plume from her back. If ever he needed help, he had only to set it alight and she would instantly come to him.

Some years later, when he himself was awaiting a first-born son, Zal remembered the great bird's promise, for the pregnancy was prolonged and his wife was growing weaker. At once the simurgh appeared, advising him to have the child removed from the womb by a skilled doctor – in other words, for a Caesarean section to be performed. Zal and his wife followed the advice, also taking advantage of medicinal herbs the simurgh had provided to heal the wounds, and were rewarded with a fine son. In time the boy grew up to become Persia's greatest hero, the warrior Rustam.

> "The abandoned child was found by the simurgh and carried back to her nest, where she raised him as part of her own feathered brood."

The story of Zal illustrates the simurgh's high standing in Persia. Its origins seem to have lain in an earlier mythical creature, the saena. In Zoroastrian creation stories, the saena dwelled in the branches of the Tree of Life, flapping its wings to distribute the seeds from which all plant life on Earth ultimately grew.

In later times the bird, which was usually solitary although it could be of either gender, took on the role it played in the Zal story, of a creature of superhuman wisdom and power. It was particularly associated with healing, helping to close Rustam's wounds when, near the end of his life, he fought the younger champion Isfandiyar. It also inherited from its mythic origins a link with the fertility of the soil, while its role as ruler of the birds allowed it to serve as a mediator between the realms of Earth and sky.

The stories of Zal and Rustam were recounted in Persia's great national epic, *The Shahnameh* ("Book of Kings"), but the simurgh also had a central role in another literary classic. Farid al-din Attar's twelfth-century masterpiece *The Parliament of the Birds* made it the object of a metaphysical quest. Setting out to find the legendary King of the Birds, birds of every species embark on a long and dangerous journey. Many fall by the wayside, but thirty of the most coura-

geous pilgrims reach the remote peak where the simurgh (whose name can be interpreted to mean "thirty birds") is said to live. There they make an unexpected discovery: collectively they themselves, purified by labour and suffering, are the simurgh, and a part of the divine creature lives in each one of them.

Harpies Winged hags who defiled all that they touched

Appearance
Originally wind-goddesses depicted with long, loose hair, they later became foul, vulture-like birds with the heads, torsos and arms of women.

Size
Usually shown the size of large birds of prey.

Lifespan
Lengthy, but not immortal.

Powers
The ability to move between the human world and the Underworld, and powers to foresee the future.

Habitat
Originally in eastern Thrace, but driven by the Argonauts to the Strophades – two small islets south of Zakinthos in the Ionian Sea. An alternative tradition had them living in a cave on Crete.

Greek myth was often harsh on women. Its repertoire of female monsters included the snake-haired Gorgons (see pages 154–155) and the implacable Furies (see page 34) as well as such dangerous enchantresses as Medea and Circe. Yet none of its creations was as misogynistic as the harpies.

Like the sirens, the harpies were birds with women's heads and upper bodies, but the resemblance ended there. The sirens may have been lethal, but they were also alluring, attracting sailors with the enchantment of their songs. The harpies, in contrast, were simply revolting. Embodiments of insatiable greed, they swooped on diners, snatching food from their hands and fouling the dishes laid out before them. Much emphasis was laid on their vileness: their horrible screeching, the disgusting stench they emitted, the excrement smeared over their unwashed underparts.

The filthy hags described in literature seem remote from the harpies' original incarnation as wind-goddesses, described by Hesiod as "lovely-haired". Their name derived from the verb *harpazein*, "to snatch", and they seem to have started life as personifications of storm winds. Homer mentioned a single harpy and Hesiod two, but by later times they generally formed a trinity, like the Gorgons, Fates and Furies. The names assigned to them – Aello ("Storm Wind"), Ocypete ("Swift-flying"), Celaino ("Dark") – emphasized their tempestuous natures.

The harriers harried

The harpies are now best remembered for their part in the hero myths, most notably that of Jason. At the start of their quest for the Golden Fleece, the Argonauts stopped in eastern Thrace at the kingdom of blind King Phineus, known for his prophetic powers. The king agreed to give them advice, but only on condition that they helped rid him of the harpies, who were making his life a misery by stealing food from his table. He and his courtiers had been reduced almost to starvation by their depradations. (Parenthetically, the revisionist historian Diodorus Siculus chose to challenge this story, insinuating instead that Phineus's Scythian second wife was actually responsible for the removal of the food, seeking thereby to rid herself of her sightless and unwanted husband.)

The harpies had proved invulnerable to normal means of defence, but Jason had a special weapon at his disposal. Among the band of heroes he had assembled were Calais and Zetes, two sons of Boreas the North Wind, who were winged like the harpies themselves. These two pursued their quarry across the Aegean Sea and on over the Greek mainland until they reached the Strophades – islets south of Zakinthos in the Ionian Sea. There the harpies begged for their lives, and their pursuers agreed to leave them in peace when they promised to stay where they were and to trouble Phineus no more.

They were still living on the Strophades when Aeneas encountered them en route from Troy to Italy, as described in Virgil's *Aeneid*. Their

33

personal hygiene had not improved in the intervening years. To quote John Dryden's translation, "Monsters more fierce offended Heav'n ne'er sent/From hell's abyss, for human punishment:/With virgin faces, but with wombs obscene,/Foul paunches, and with ordure still unclean." These aerial pests not merely spoiled the travellers' dinner but also cursed them, using their prophetic powers to forecast starvation for them in the months ahead. Chastened, the Trojans upped anchor and fled.

Elsewhere in Greek myth, the harpies played a different but equally terrifying role as emissaries of the Underworld, sent to snatch souls to Hades. Some such duty seems to be implied by their representation on the "Harpy Tomb", a fifth-century BCE funerary pillar from Lycia in what

THE FEARSOME FURIES

The Harpies were linked in myth to another ghastly trio, the Erinyes or Furies. According to at least one myth – that of the daughters of Pandareus – the Harpies served as the Furies' emissaries, bringing them human victims whom they subsequently enslaved.

There were three Furies, known respectively as Tisiphone, Megaera and Allecto, and they were said to have been born soon after the world's creation from the blood spilled when Cronos castrated his father Uranus. Thereafter their mission was to track down all those who, like Cronos, had visited acts of violence on their own relatives. Spirits of retribution, they also punished perjurers and individuals who violated the laws of hospitality.

The Furies' primordial birth meant that they predated Zeus and the Olympian gods and never fell under their control. They lived in the Underworld, operating to their own implacable remit. Immortal and unforgiving, they pursued their appointed task of hunting the guilty, taking no mitigating circumstances into account. Terrifying to look at, they had dog's heads, bloodshot eyes, bats' wings and snakes for hair, and they carried torches to seek out their quarry and whips with which to scourge them. Their victims, who included the patricide Oedipus and the mother-killer Orestes, were driven either to insanity or else to their deaths.

Despite being driven mad, Orestes eventually found respite, largely through the support of Apollo. Instructed to plead his case before the Areopagus, the chief law-giving body at Athens, he was absolved from guilt, largely because the god himself acted as his defence counsel. Thereafter the Furies unwillingly ended their persecution, and were rewarded with a small shrine at the base of the Areopagite Hill. Athenians also gave them the euphemistic title of Eumenides or "Kindly Ones", widely used thereafter by cautious citizens eager to avert their terrible wrath.

is now Turkey. The carvings show them as winged bird-women clutching tiny human figures to their breasts.

Memories of this function survive in the sad story of the daughters of Pandareus. This native of Miletus had the temerity to steal the golden mastiff made by the metal-working god Hephaestus to guard the infant Zeus. For his crime Pandareus was hunted down and killed by the gods (some said he was turned to stone). Yet his death was not enough to sate the divine wrath. He had two beautiful daughters, Merope and Cleothera, who had been reared by Aphrodite herself on curds, honey and sweet wine, and granted wisdom and skills by Hera and Artemis. Once he had grown to maturity, Zeus sent the Harpies to carry off these paragons, delivering them into

> "Embodiments of insatiable greed, they swooped on diners, snatching food from their hands and fouling the dishes laid out before them."

the hands of the Furies to suffer vicariously for their father's crime.

Even so, it was the Harpies' foulness that mostly survived. In his *Inferno*, Dante made them the guardians of suicides and other self-harmers. And in the medieval bestiaries they featured as symbols of avarice, victims of their own insatiable appetites, which drove them and those they plagued to the borders of insanity and beyond.

35

KURANGAITUKU, THE MAORI BIRD-WOMAN

Maori myth also had stories of a fearsome bird-woman. Her name was Kurangaituku, a huge, winged woman covered all over in feathers, and unlike the harpies she lived a solitary life. She is best remembered now for her part in a favourite hero legend concerning the doings of a put-upon youth named Hatupatu. Escaping from brothers who had long bullied and even sought to kill him, he encountered Kurangaituku, who was busy spearing birds with her sharp beak. Hatupatu inadvertently struck the bird-woman with his spear, which provoked her to capture him and confine him in a cave, where his future looked no brighter than that of Ulysses' companions in the lair of Polyphemus the Cyclops (see page 62). Like the heroes of *The Odyssey*, however, he managed to escape, in his case taking with him Kurangaituku's fine cloaks and *taiaha* (fighting-staff). The bird-woman pursued him, but he escaped her clutches by reciting a magic chant and hiding inside a boulder. People still point out a split rock by the roadside near Atiamuri on New Zealand's North Island as the spot where the adventure took place.

Fenghuang Chinese bird of good omen

There was no sight that gladdened the heart of a Chinese emperor more than a fenghuang, but few ever got to see one. For the birds were propitious, appearing only in times of prosperity and peace. Their presence was a sign that the ruler, through his judiciousness and wisdom, had won the approval of the gods. As such, the birds were said to have clustered in the gardens of the legendary Huang Di, or Yellow Emperor, a culture hero credited with bringing the benefits of civilization to the nation.

One reason why the bird symbolized harmony was because it balanced the forces of yin and yang in its own body. In the earliest representations, dating as far back as 5000 BCE, it was depicted as two separate creatures, the male feng and the female huang, shown facing each other in early jade ornaments. By historical times, though, the two had come together in a single being.

Thereafter the feminine part of the fenghuang's character tended to predominate. The bird was the symbol of China's empresses just as the dragon was of the emperors. The mythical Queen Mother of the West was said to ride on one when travelling around the paradisial mountain kingdom where she guarded the Peaches of Immortality.

The fenghuang also featured alongside the dragon in early Chinese cosmology, both numbering (with the tiger and the tortoise) among the propitious animals associated with the four compass points. The fenghuang's direction was south, which linked it to the summer season and the element of fire. As a result, the most prominent of the many brilliant hues that lit up its extravagant plumage was red, leading it to be known as the Red Bird of the South.

The fenghuang had a mammalian counterpart in the qilin or Chinese unicorn (see pages 104–105), which similarly appeared only in auspicious reigns. It too became proverbial as a symbol of good times, most often invoked in their absence. Confucius is recorded in the *Analects* as complaining in a time of dejection, "The fenghuang does not come; it is all over with me!", a cry of despair whose Western equivalent might be "There's no light at the end of the tunnel".

Firebird Radiant prize of Russian folklore

Appearance
Magical bird with glowing, brilliantly coloured feathers.

Size
Roughly that of a peacock.

Lifespan
Unknown.

Powers
Had feathers that shone brightly enough to light up a room, even when plucked.

Habitat
The forests of old Russia.

Gorgeously plumed in shades of red, yellow and orange, the firebird of Russian folklore was so radiant that its feathers continued to glow even when plucked or shed. Small wonder, then, that the bird itself was sought after as the goal of quests. Fabled but rarely seen, it became a sort of animate equivalent of the Holy Grail, magically beautiful and almost impossible to obtain.

Sometimes the bird played an active role in the stories, usually as a deus ex machina appearing from nowhere to rescue the hero from danger. In one folktale it brought the Water of Life to a prince slain by his own wicked brothers. In another it rescued a merchant's son from the clutches of the cannibalistic witch Baba Yaga (see pages 112–113), carrying him on its back to safety over the seas.

Usually, though, its role was passive. The most famous firebird story of all told how a huntsman found one of its feathers and, despite warnings from his horse (which was gifted with the power of speech), took it back proudly for his master the czar. As the horse had foreseen, however, the gift only whetted

the avaricious ruler's appetite, and he immediately ordered the man on pain of death to bring back the bird itself. In despair, the huntsman looked to the horse for advice and was instructed to strew corn over a field and wait. When the firebird duly arrived to eat the grain, the horse trapped one of its wings under its hoof, allowing the huntsman to capture it and take it back to court.

The adventures of Prince Ivan

Another favourite tale told of a king who set his three sons to capture the firebird when it took to stealing golden apples from his orchard. The two elder brothers failed completely in the task, but the youngest, Prince Ivan, first managed to snatch one of its magical feathers, then eventually succeeded in catching the bird itself – but only after much suffering and once more thanks to the aid of a talking animal, in this case a grey wolf. The story ended with Ivan being attacked by his envious siblings, who killed him and then falsely claimed to have found the bird themselves. The wolf soon put paid to their evil schemes, however, bringing the prince back to life to win redress – and, of course, to marry a beautiful princess.

The great twentieth-century composer Igor Stravinsky drew on such fairytales for his ballet *The Firebird*. The storyline borrowed the character of Prince Ivan from the traditional accounts, but made his animal helper the firebird itself. Between them, the two manage to overcome the wiles of the wicked sorcerer Kaschkei the Deathless, freeing no fewer than thirteen princesses from the enchantment he has cast over them. The childlike simplicity of the plot, contrasting with the sophistication of the music and the stunning modernism of Diaghilev's production, caused a sensation when the ballet was premiered in Paris in 1910, helping to change the course of European music as well as to give new legs, in the most literal sense, to one of Russian folklore's more memorable creations.

39

Tengu Fearsome birdman to be angered at your peril

Appearance
Grotesque birdman with glittering eyes and a long, beaklike nose, often bright red. Some tengu are semi-human in appearance, but others have feathered bodies; all have malign expressions and the wings and talons of birds of prey.

Size
Variable. The legendary king of the tengu was said to be of giant size, but others are depicted as smaller than humans.

Lifespan
Unknown, but thought to exceed the normal human span.

Powers
Able to walk and fly. Skilled in martial arts and swordsmanship.

Habitat
Wooded mountain regions of Japan.

Lone travellers wandering in the forested mountains of Japan used to glance nervously about them at nightfall, fearing the sight of a pair of glowing eyes staring back through the foliage. Chances were that the creature might be a tengu – one of a race of spirits, half bird and half human, that haunted remote woodlands. Said to be emanations of Susano, the Shinto embodiment of male aggression, tengu were at best suspicious of strangers entering their domain and at worst lethally hostile.

Yoshitsune and the king of the tengu
The best-known story concerning the spirits comes from the epic of Yoshitsune, a real-life player in the struggle between the Taira and Minamoto clans for control of twelfth-century Japan. As a boy he was sent to live in a monastery by the Taira warlord responsible for his father's death. There he nurtured fantasies of revenge, wandering alone into the woods to practise swordplay.

One evening, as he sparred with branches, he was startled by a clap of thunder above his head. Looking up, he found himself gazing at the king of the tengu himself, come to see who was disturbing the solitude of the forest. Bravely the youngster stood his ground. Smiling at his boldness, the giant winged figure offered to guide him in the art of swordsmanship. Under the tengu's tuition Yoshitsune grew up to be a great warrior who would in time humble his Taira enemies.

Yoshitsune was unusually lucky, for most humans who encountered tengu lived to regret the experience. Often the spirits were merely mischievous – for instance, whirling unwary individuals up into the air for unplanned flights above the treetops. Sometimes they kidnapped people for longer periods, and then their victims usually returned at best dazed and confused and at worst completely out of their minds. One such was a samurai called Kiuchi Heizayemon, who was found crouching on a temple roof, having been beaten and then rushed through the air for what seemed like many hours. It took Kiuchi three days to recover from his ordeal and recount his experiences.

Deadly retribution

Tengu were easily offended. A wrestler named Tobikawa made the mistake of dressing up as a tengu and perching on a branch as a practical joke; for his temerity he was dashed to the ground and killed. Another rash individual attracted the attention of a tengu when he defiled the sanctity of a roadside Shinto shrine. Mistaking the feathered newcomer for a bird, the intruder picked up his musket and fired off a shot. The tengu responded by touching him lightly with a twig, whereupon he burst into flames and was burned to ashes.

Such beliefs were taken seriously in Japan at least as late as 1860. In that year the ruling Edo shogun made a visit to Nikko, north of modern-day Tokyo, where the great Tokugawa shoguns Ieyasu and Iemitsu are buried. An English visitor reported that local officials put up signs around the site warning local tengu to stay away, even specifying the mountains where they could lawfully resort during the visit.

Griffin Eagle-headed lion

42

Appearance
A lion with an eagle's foreparts, wings, beak and sometimes talons, at least on its front legs. Equipped with prominent, upturned ears that let it hear the slightest sound.

Size
Vast. "A body greater than eight lions", according to Sir John Mandeville's fanciful *Travels*.

Lifespan
Unrecorded.

Powers
Untameable and mighty, strong enough to overpower elephants and tigers. Some accounts speak of griffins carrying off horses and their riders at one swoop.

Habitat
According to the Greek chronicler Herodotus, the northern parts of Scythia, where they guarded hordes of gold. An alternative, medieval tradition located them in the wastes of India, where they were said to live on mountaintops.

Combining the body of a lion, the mightiest of land animals, with the foreparts of an eagle, the lord of the air, the griffin was an early symbol of power. Its origins lie deep in the mythology of the ancient Middle East. In Sumerian myth winged lions were associated with the weather god Iskur, and were shown with streams of rainwater issuing from their mouths. In Old Kingdom Egypt, similar-looking beasts attended victorious rulers in steles showing pharaohs bestriding the dead bodies of their enemies. By Assyrian times they had attained the status of heraldic guardians, shown in pairs on their hind legs flanking winged gods.

Jealous guardians of gold
Ancient Greece also viewed the griffin as a guardian, carving its image on tombs to protect the dead. Yet the chief Greek contribution to the griffin saga was to first record reports of the animal's existence, establishing an enduring tradition that it lived in remote parts of the world. The chief source was Herodotus. In his encyclopedic *Histories*, written in the fifth century BCE, he recorded a story originating in Scythia, the northernmost part of the Greek world. The Scythians told of a race of one-eyed people known as the Arimaspians, who lived to the north. The Arimaspians spent much of their time seeking gold, which was plentiful in their lands, but they could obtain it only by stealing it from griffins, which guarded it jealously. Unlikely though the story sounded, it obviously had some currency at the time, for the tragedian Aeschylus made reference to it in his play *Prometheus Bound*, which slightly predated Herodotus's work.

The story incorporated the griffin's traditional role as guardian, and it may be that the Scythians deliberately invented it to protect their very real gold deposits. They may also have tried to bolster its veracity by passing off dinosaur bones, also found in the region, as griffin remains. In recent years, scholars have pointed out similarities between Proceratops skulls excavated in central Asia and subsequent depictions of griffins.

Whatever its origins, the story quickly took root. Even though some

authorities, including Pliny and the geographer Strabo, expressed scepticism, other writers accepted it uncritically, and it fed into medieval natural histories that passed the griffin off as a real creature rather than a myth. Further confirmation, if any were needed, was provided by a mistranslation in the Vulgate (the Latin version of the Bible), which included the griffin in Moses' list of animals considered unfit to eat. With biblical authority behind it, few commentators dared question the creature's authenticity for the next thousand years.

Between truth and fiction

The griffin continued also to provide good copy for writers of fiction. The authors of the fanciful epics of Alexander the Great, which almost rivalled the Arthurian cycle in popularity in the Middle Ages, came up with a tale that joined the Scythians' story as a stock part of griffin lore. They claimed that the Greek emperor, eager to experience flight, came up with an ingenious invention. He attached four griffins to a receptacle large enough to hold him, then persuaded them to take to the air by dangling lumps of meat on poles just beyond the reach of their jaws. As they beat their wings in frustration, seeking to reach the bait, Alexander was successfully raised heavenward. Some versions altered the tale to end in failure, enabling the authors to point a moral of ambition overreaching itself; by trying to fly, they claimed, the emperor, Icarus-like, had sought to assert for himself powers that were rightly divine.

Throughout the Middle Ages the griffin had a double life. On the one hand it kept its original role as a heraldic guardian and an image of kingly power – Edward III, for one, had the beast engraved on his private seal. On the other, it was regarded as a genuine phenomenon of nature, illustrating the wonders of God's creation. One early geographer described how hunters killed griffins by luring them onto platforms of woven reed baited with meat; the mats

---

THE HIPPOGRIFF — A LEARNED JOKE

"Griffins must be mating with horses", the Roman poet Virgil wrote in his *Eclogues* of 37 BCE to indicate a total improbability, much as we might say "And pigs might fly". For any reader of the time would have known that griffins were born enemies of the entire equine race, perhaps because their sworn foe, the one-eyed Arimaspians of northern Scythia, came on horseback to steal their gold (see page 42). So the Renaissance poet Ariosto was playing a learned joke when he invented the hippogriff, a flying horse born of the union of a griffin and a mare. The creature first appeared in his mock-epic *Orlando Furioso*, which describes the madness of the hero Orlando, driven out of his wits for love. Only in a seriously deranged world, the poet seems to be saying, could such an unlikely creature ever even be imagined.

were then set on fire, so that the animals fell through, their wings singed, onto the prongs of tridents hidden beneath. The learned St Hildegard of Bingen reported that they laid their eggs in narrow caves to keep them safe from lions, which would otherwise have trampled them. There was an active trade at the time in griffin claws and eggs, which were regarded as precious relics; examples preserved in the treasury of St Cuthbert in Durham have turned out to be, respectively, ibis horns and ostrich eggs. Robert the Pious, Capetian king of France at the turn of the first millennium, kept a supposed griffin's egg in a silver reliquary and made barons swear oaths over it.

A monstrous invention

With the dawning of the Age of Reason in the sixteenth and seventeenth centuries, such tales finally fell into disrepute. Sceptics pointed out the lack of first-hand evidence for the birds' existence, and geographers denied any knowledge of their presence in the lands where they were supposed to live. The English man of letters Sir Thomas Browne caught the new mood when he opined of griffins that "the invention is monstrous, not much inferior to the figment of sphinx, chimaera and harpies".

Robbed of their actuality, griffins were henceforward restricted to heraldry and to storytelling, where they were soon reduced to the status of fantasy creatures used to entertain children. A gryphon (sic – the spelling "griffon" is also sometimes used) famously features in *Alice in Wonderland*, where the bird performs a dance, the Lobster Quadrille, with its melancholy friend the Mock Turtle. Harry Potter's schoolhouse at Hogwarts is called Gryffindor, suggesting the French *griffon d'or* or "golden griffin", although its emblem is actually a lion, and the creatures also feature in Aslan's army in C.S. Lewis's *Chronicles of Narnia*. The griffin that appears in T.H. White's *Once and Future King* is a ferocious monster with which the young Arthur does battle – a rare reminder of the days when the creatures were considered genuinely formidable, bringing together in one body the fiercest aspects of the top predators of earth and sky.

Phoenix Regenerative bird that rose from its own ashes

Appearance
Pierre de Beauvais claimed "it has a crest like a peacock's, its breast and throat are resplendent in red, toward its tail it is blue as the clear sky".

Size
According to Herodotus, "most like an eagle in shape and size".

Lifespan
Self-renewing. It died every 500 years or so (1,461, according to Tacitus), only to be reborn from its own funeral pyre.

Powers
Immortality through constant rebirth.

Habitat
Arabia.

The phoenix's origins lay in distorted classical accounts of ancient Egyptian rites. The Egyptians worshipped a bird called the benu, depicted as a heron or stork, that was sacred to the sun god Ra. The benu was said to be self-generating, born from a sacred fire that burned in Ra's temple at Heliopolis – an obvious symbol of the Sun itself, which dies in its own flames each evening to be born again the following dawn.

Word of this creature reached Herodotus in garbled form. In his account the bird lived and died in Arabia, to the east of Egypt and hence in the direction of the rising Sun. With obvious disbelief he recorded a story he had heard to the effect that the young bird then wrapped its dead parent's body in a casing of myrrh and carried it to Heliopolis for immolation.

Other classical writers added extra details to his account. The dying bird was said to prepare its own funeral pyre by building a nest of aromatic herbs, then to set fire to it by striking a stone with its beak. Tacitus claimed that this self-immolation occurred once every 1,461 years, relating it to the Sothic cycle that linked the 365-day Egyptian year to the heliacal rising of the dog star, Sirius.

In its fully fledged version, however, the phoenix legend was a Christian creation. From at least the time of Claudian in the fourth century CE, people claimed that there was only one phoenix – one that regenerated itself after a 500-year life-cycle. When it felt death nearing, it made its pyre from frankincense, myrrh and other spices. (Other sources maintained the Egyptian connection by claiming it flew to Heliopolis in Egypt, where a priest prepared an altar topped with kindling.) Striking a spark with its beak, it fanned the flames with its wings until it was consumed.

One day later, a small, maggot-like creature would be seen in the ashes. By the second day it grew feathers and took on a recognizably bird-like appearance, and on the third day the phoenix itself emerged fully fledged. The story provided an obvious analogy for supporters of Christianity, who saw in it a direct parallel with Christ's resurrection and a metaphor for spiritual rebirth.

ROC Gigantic bird of Arab legend

Appearance
Vast bird of prey, "just like an eagle but of the most colossal size", according to Marco Polo.

Size
Polo gave its wingspan as 48 feet (14.6m) across, with wing feathers 24 feet (7.3m) long.

Lifespan
Not known.

Powers
Big and strong enough to carry an elephant in its talons.

Habitat
The Middle East and Madagascar; one account spoke of "the China seas".

In Sinbad's second voyage, as described in the *1,001 Nights*, the sailor fell asleep ashore when his ship made landfall at a remote island and woke to find his companions had left without him. Exploring the neighbourhood he found a pure white dome with no door in it, fifty paces around. As he wondered at the sight, the sky above him darkened and he looked up to see an enormous bird descending on what he now realized to be its egg. Thinking quickly, he lashed himself to the bird's leg with his turban. Never sensing his presence, the great bird eventually rose into the air again and carried him off to a distant mountaintop.

The tale is probably the best-known source for accounts of the roc, a legendary bird of vast size possibly related to the Persian simurgh (see pages 30–31). The *1,001 Nights* in fact had other references to the creature. One short episode described an encounter a North African merchant had with the bird in "the China seas". He too was amazed by the sight of an unhatched egg, said to be 100 cubits (about 150ft/45m) long. Breaking it open, he secured a feather from the unhatched chick inside that was large enough to hold a skinful of water. As he and his shipmates sailed away they were pursued by the vengeful mother bird, which dropped a huge boulder on the vessel, fortunately missing her target.

Marco Polo in Madagascar
Following in the tradition of such travellers' tales, Marco Polo located rocs on the island of Madagascar, which he visited in the 1290s. Local people told him of a vast, eagle-like bird that had the habit of lifting elephants up in the air

---

ANZU AND THE TABLETS OF DESTINY

Tales of gigantic birds go far back in Middle Eastern myth. Mesopotamian peoples told stories of a vast, lion-headed eagle known as the anzu that stole the Tablets of Destiny from the sky god Enlil. There were different versions of the way in which they were returned. Some said the god Marduk killed the thief, others that the hero Ninurta attacked it and made it drop them. A third legend told how another hero, Lugalbanda, won the bird's gratitude by feeding delicacies to its chick, which he found in an unguarded nest. In return the anzu granted him a wish, which he used to gain the boon of running any distance without feeling fatigue.

in its talons and then dropping them so it could feed on the pulp. Polo himself had seen a roc's feather, brought back by envoys to the court of the Great Khan, whose quill measured twice the width of his own hand. Scholars have speculated that this might have been a frond of the raffia palm, passed off as a roc's feather to impress the Chinese visitors.

The link with Madagascar has set cryptozoologists seeking possible models for the bird among the extinct fauna of the island. One candidate is the Madagascan crowned hawk-eagle (*Stephanoaetus mahery*), which died out when humans settled on the island sometime before 1000 CE, and which was large enough to feed on giant lemurs. Another is *Aepyornis maximus*, the Elephant bird. This huge, flightless relative of the ostrich, which may have survived as late as the sixteenth century, stood as much as 10 feet (3m) tall and weighed half a tonne. Even if the bird itself, with its long neck and tiny wings, could hardly have been mistaken for an eagle, researchers have suggested it might have been taken for the chick of an even larger, winged parent. The eggs of the Elephant bird were also impressive, although hardly dome-sized; one has been found measuring over 3 feet (1m) in circumference.

"Local people told him of a vast, eagle-like bird that had the habit of lifting elephants up in the air in its talons and then dropping them so it could feed on the pulp."

Shedu & Lammasu Winged guardian spirits

Appearance
Shedu took the form of winged bulls with human faces; lammasu were winged lions.

Size
Monumentally large. Those guarding the palace of Sargon at Khorsabad stood 14ft (4.4m) tall.

Lifespan
As spirit beings, not subject to mortality.

Powers
Protective spirits, they guarded houses and palaces against malicious demons.

Habitat
Ancient Mesopotamia and Persia.

The people of ancient Mesopotamia inhabited a demon-haunted universe. Living at a time when life expectancy was little more than thirty years, they grew up all too aware of the frailties of the human condition. In a world where many disasters, from drought to pestilence, were beyond their control, people instinctively tended to blame misfortunes on the actions of evil spirits.

The demons that afflicted them were innumerable and often invisible. Some had names. Lamashtu, a hideous, lion-headed hag, was responsible for miscarriages, still-births and cot deaths; Rabisu, "the Croucher", waylaid passers-by in dark alleys; Lilitu, the origin of the Hebrew Lilith, seduced men in their sleep. Others were anonymous, like the fearsome *gallas* or "constables", emissaries of the dread Ereshkigal, queen of the Underworld, who dragged transgressors into her dark realm. Most ubiquitous of all were the multiple unnamed household demons who spread disease and discord in people's homes.

Naturally enough, people looked for protectors who could guard them against the ministrations of the evil spirits. Foremost among these good genies were the shedu and lammasu, whose effigies stood guard outside palaces and temples. Both were hybrid creatures, combining human heads with the bodies of animals that symbolized power: bulls in the case of the shedu, lions for lammasu.

Emblems of the gods
Scholars have speculated that the bulls depicted in the shedu were in fact bison, which had died out in Mesopotamia at the start of the historic period; their memory was kept fresh in heroic legends. Some such provenance seems to be indicated by the thick hair carved onto the statues, covering the creatures' chest, neck and flanks. As for lions, they were common in Mesopotamia at the time, as suggested by the celebrated lion-hunt reliefs, commemorating the exploits of King Ashurbanipal of Assyria, which are now on view in the British Museum.

Both creatures had links with major deities, which may have increased their protective power: bulls were emblematic of the storm god Ishkur or Adad; lions of the sun god Shamash and the warrior goddess Ishtar. Their mere presence was tutelary, as suggested by a relief from the palace at Khorsabad that shows a shedu as a guardian-angel figure accompanying an expedition bringing precious cedar-wood from Lebanon. In contrast, seizing an enemy's shedu was a mark of conquest; Ashurbanipal listed the removal of those guarding the temple of Elam in the victory inscriptions that celebrated his capture of the city in 640 BCE.

On a more humble scale, too, ordinary householders sought to benefit from the beasts' custodial influence. It was common practice to bury clay tablets bearing their images under the threshold of people's homes, where they served as tireless guard-dogs, constantly on the watch for spiritual intruders.

Mothman Flying humanoid or urban legend?

Appearance
A winged human figure with glowing red eyes.

Size
6.5–7ft (about 2m) tall, according to witnesses.

Lifespan
Unknown.

Powers
Flight and, according to some theories, precognition.

Habitat
Point Pleasant, West Virginia, and surrounding locales.

In late 1966 stories began to circulate in and around Point Pleasant, West Virginia, a small town on the Ohio River, about a strange and terrifying figure seen in the surrounding countryside. The most detailed account came from two couples who had been driving at night past a disused munitions factory. Noticing two red spots glowing in the dark, they stopped the car, only to discover that the lights were actually the eyes of a creature described as "shaped like a man but bigger, maybe six and a half or seven feet tall, with big wings folded against its back". Terrified, they drove to a nearby county courthouse to alert the deputy on duty, and the being flew alongside their car for part of the way.

Their story appeared in the local media, and other sightings followed over the next couple of weeks. Some people simply saw the creature standing or walking, but at least one other witness claimed that it had flown beside his car, again in the vicinity of the same factory. Thereafter the reports became

PANIC IN NEW JERSEY

Another American flying creature inhabiting the murky penumbra between reality and legend is the Jersey Devil, which terrorized the Pine Barrens of southern New Jersey for a week in 1909. Eyewitness accounts compared the beast to animals as diverse as a crane and a kangaroo. One of the most detailed described it as being about 3.5 feet (1m) tall and having a head like a collie dog and a face like a horse, with a long neck, wings about 2 feet (0.6m) wide, and back legs like a crane's but with horse's hooves. It walked on these limbs, holding up two short front legs with paws on them. Its tracks were found in the snow covering the region at the time, sometimes on rooftops, and it was also seen flying.

Similar sightings of a winged creature had been reported in the area for at least a century before. Among those claiming to have seen it were the Revolutionary War hero Stephen Decatur and Joseph Bonaparte, Napoleon's eldest brother. Occasional observations continue to this day, but with nothing like the frequency of the 1909 panic, when armed posses hunted the beast and some schools and businesses were temporarily closed down.

more sporadic, largely dying away after December 15, 1967, when the town suffered its worst-ever disaster with the collapse of the Silver Bridge, a suspension bridge linking Point Pleasant with Kanauga across the Ohio River. The bridge was clogged with rush-hour traffic at the time and forty-six people died.

Eight years later a Fortean researcher named John Keel published a book, *The Mothman Prophecies*, linking the two events and also connecting them to other paranormal activities that allegedly occurred in the area at the time. The book in turn became the inspiration for a Richard Gere film of the same name.

Both book and film took a supernatural view of the phenomena, which Keel linked to theories about UFOs.

Other researchers have pointed out similarities with accounts of humanoid flying creatures from elsewhere in the world. In the 1970s reports circulated around the Cornish village of Mawnan of a large, owl-like figure with red eyes and pincer-like claws, promptly dubbed "Owlman". Parallels have also been drawn with Spring-Heeled Jack, a legendary figure in Victorian England, who leaped out unexpectedly to shock young women and supposedly evaded capture by jumping over high walls.

Part 2
Beasts
of the
Earth

Behemoth Monstrous denizen of the marshes

Appearance
Strong and powerful, with "bones that are tubes of brass and limbs like bars of iron".

Size
Originally hippopotamus-sized. In later belief, unimaginably vast – the apocryphal Second Book of Esdras claimed that the oceans were not large enough to hold him and Leviathan together.

Lifespan
Unspecified.

Powers
Sturdy and tough – "Behold the strength in his loins and the power in the muscles of his belly!"

Habitat
Rivers and marshes, where he lies "under the lotus plants".

56

Today the word "behemoth" is used to refer to anything exceptionally large and weighty, from a giant truck to a Hollywood epic; it is also the name of a Polish death-metal band. Yet the original Behemoth was one of the most specific of all the creatures of the Mythic Bestiary, for its origins can be traced to a single source – the Old Testament Book of Job. The text consists of a conversation between Job and Jehovah, in the course of which God, speaking out of a whirlwind, displays his own power by describing the mighty Behemoth, "which I made as I made you".

The word itself simply means "animals" in Hebrew, and is what is known as an intensive plural, denoting a single animal of exceptional size. Jehovah then goes on to describe a powerful beast that "eats grass like an ox" and that lives "in the covert of the reeds and in the marsh" as well as in rivers: "If the river is turbulent, he is not frightened; Jordan itself would have no terrors for that gaping mouth".

The words would seem to indicate a hippopotamus, although some authorities believe they could refer to an elephant. Yet "behemoth" came to stand for much more. For Jehovah goes on to speak of the sea beast Leviathan (see pages 200–203), and it becomes obvious that the two have a symbolic significance as the most fearsome denizens, respectively, of the land and of the sea.

Later texts took this larger sense and pushed it to extremes. The apocryphal Second Book of Esdras speaks of God creating Behemoth and Leviathan on the fifth day of creation, claiming that the waters of the ocean were not large enough to contain them both. Behemoth then became the primordial land monster, paralleling Leviathan's role as the primeval sea serpent.

MIGHTY BAHAMUT

In Arab legend Behemoth was transmuted into Bahamut, a creature of unimaginable size; when Isa (the Islamic name for Jesus) was granted a vision of the beast, he fell into a faint that lasted for three days and nights. Other fundamental transformations also occurred along the way, for Bahamut is described as a gigantic fish supporting the Earth – on its back stands a bull with 4,000 eyes that in turn supports a mountain of ruby on which stands the angel upholding the world.

Giants The mighty men that were of old

58

Appearance
Extra-large beings in human form, portrayed in a wide spectrum of ways, from superheroes to subhuman cavemen.

Size
By definition very large, although the scale can range from the cosmic to anything above 7 feet, 6 inches (2.3m) – the definition generally applied to human giants. The biblical Goliath was "six cubits and a span" (over 9 feet/2.75m) in height; a skeleton dug up by the Spartans in classical times and claimed to be that of the hero Orestes measured more than 10 feet (3.2m).

Lifespan
In legend, giants can be extraordinarily long-lived, but in real life people of exceptional stature tend to die young.

Powers
Unusual strength, often counterbalanced in folklore by dim-witted stupidity.

Habitat
All parts of the globe, although certain regions such as Patagonia at the southern tip of the American continent were particularly famed for their gigantic inhabitants.

Some mythic beasts seem to spring from the farther reaches of the human imagination, but giants require little explanation. There is a natural curiosity about people of unusual size, and every culture has tales of people of exceptional stature. The main difference lies in how they are regarded: as mighty helpers or as fearsome adversaries.

More surprising, perhaps, is the prevalence of stories of early races of giants in many of the world's mythologies. The Greeks had several such groups – Titans (see box) and Hecatonchires (Hundred-handed Ones) as well as giants – who struggled for supremacy with the Olympian gods. Norse myth had similar accounts of the struggles between the Aesir (the ruling gods of Asgard) and the gigantic inhabitants of Jotunheim. The Celts spoke of the monstrous Fomorians, while in South America Inca legend retained the memory of a huge race swept away by a primeval flood. Even the biblical Book of Genesis preserved the memory of the Nephilim, a race of vast

THE PRIMEVAL TITANS

In Greek myth the Titans were a primeval race of giants born of the earth mother Gaia and her husband and son Uranus. In all there were twelve of them, six sons and six daughters. At their mother's urging they rose up against their abusive father, whom the youngest, Cronos, castrated with a sickle as he slept. Cronos then took his father's place as ruler of the gods. He, however, proved quite as despotic as Uranus had been, eating his own newly born children for fear that they would in turn dethrone him. But one, Zeus, escaped his father's clutches, and subsequently realized Cronos's worst fears by stirring up revolt.

The other Titans rallied behind Cronos, and for ten years war raged between them and Zeus's Olympians. When Zeus's force finally prevailed, most of the Titans were hurled down into the abyss of Tartarus. But the leader of their army, Atlas, was condemned for all eternity to bear the weight of the heavens on his shoulders, preventing the sky from falling to Earth. The Atlas Mountains of North Africa are named after him.

stature: "There were giants in the earth in those days; and also after that, when the sons of God came in to the daughters of men, and they bore children to them, the same became mighty men which were of old, men of renown."

Wars between gods and giants

The Greek version, as told by the poet Hesiod, was particularly rich in genealogical detail. Besides the Titans, the earth mother Gaia and her husband Uranus gave birth to two other sets of gigantic progeny: the Cyclopes (see pages 62–63) and the monstrous Hecatonchires. It was Uranus's kidnapping and sequestration of the Cyclopes that initially caused Gaia to incite the Titans against him. When Zeus and his Olympians had in turn subdued the Titans, they then had to deal with the Gigantes, a separate race of oversized opponents from whose name the English word "giant" derives. The Gigantomachy, or war with the giants, became a favourite theme of classical art, and it was only won when the human hero Hercules agreed to take the Olympians' side.

In later Greek myth, the chief role of giants was to provide fitting adversaries for individual gods and heroes. When Zeus lusted after the nymph Io, his wife Hera spirited her away into confinement under the gaze of the colossal, thousand-eyed Argos, known as the All-Seeing. Zeus responded by sending Hermes to lull Argos to sleep with his lyre before decapitating him with a sword. Hercules' tenth labour was to steal the cattle of the monstrous Geryon, who had three separate torsos all springing from one trunk; the hero eventually shot the giant down with a single arrow that pierced his triple breasts. Jason and his Argonauts had to evade the bronze giant Talos, whose only weak spot was a single vein in his ankle; they finally escaped his clutches when one of their number loosed an arrow that struck this "Achilles' heel".

The Norse tradition

Norse accounts of conflicts between gods and giants were the inspiration for the later folkloric tradition by which slow-witted colossi were tricked by nimbler humans. Odin, for example, used his shape-shifting powers to steal the mead of poetry from the gigantic Suttung, seducing his daughter Gunnlod along the way. When Thor faced the mighty Hrungnir, he got his servant to persuade the giant to lower his shield, telling him Thor would attack from behind; needless to say, the god then launched a frontal assault and cracked his opponent's skull with his hammer Mjollnir.

Yet there were stories too in which the gods came off worse. One told how Thor and Loki once took shelter for the night in a cave that turned out to be the discarded glove of a sleeping giant named Skrymir. When Thor tried to deal with Skrymir as he had with Hrungnir, the aggrieved colossus woke up to complain mildly that a leaf must have brushed his head, disturbing his sleep. In another, Thor competed with a giant in a drinking contest, only to find he could come nowhere near to emptying the drinking-horn he was offered. His humiliation was only eased when his opponent revealed that he had filled the horn with the waters of all the world's oceans.

Only trouble ensued when Loki – a malicious trickster god – chose to wed the giantess Angrboda. Any alliance between the inhabitants of Asgard and Jotunheim was likely to end badly, a point amply proved when Angrboda bore three monstrous children: the wolf-monster Fenrir (see pages 138–139), the world-serpent Jormungand, and the hideous Hel, who became Queen of the Underworld. Fenrir and Jormungand were both destined to play crucial roles at Ragnarok, the final, apocalyptic confrontation in which Asgard was doomed to fall to the forces of chaos.

Mighty megalith-makers

In later times giants ceased being representatives of primeval races and shrank into local legend. Sometimes they were credited with works actually undertaken by past peoples. For example, they were often held responsible for the erection of megaliths, and the medieval Danish historian Saxo Grammaticus even cited Roman ruins as evidence that giants must once have walked the Earth.

Giants also continued to haunt people's imagination in folktales. Across the world, monstrous bogeymen kept children awake at nights. The Breton Gargam, who roamed the countryside at night in search of prey, had his equivalents in the fearsome Biloko of Zaire, equipped with crocodile snouts and a taste for human flesh, and the cannibalistic Bungisngis of the Philippines, known as "He who Shows his Teeth" because he could peel his upper lip over his forehead.

Partly in reaction, an alternative tradition of good giants developed. In Celtic myth Fionn mac Cumhaill (Finn McCool) provided the model of a hero of gigantic stature; legend subsequently

---

THE COLOSSUS OF CORNWALL

According to the twelfth-century author Geoffrey of Monmouth, whose fanciful *Historia Regum Britanniae* ("History of the Kings of Britain") set out to give Britain a legendary pedigree comparable to that of ancient Rome or Troy, Gogmagog was the leader of a race of giants inhabiting ancient Cornwall. When Brutus – a classical hero who, in Geoffrey's account, was the true founder of the British nation – first arrived on the island, he gave a war-leader named Corineus the task of defeating the giants. In a climactic confrontation, Corineus challenged Gogmagog to a wrestling match and threw him to his death over a cliff, supposedly somewhere near Plymouth. Corineus thus staked out his claim to the duchy of Cornwall.

Gogmagog's name drew on the biblical tradition of Gog and Magog, enemy nations that will be defeated by the Israelites in an apocalyptic confrontation in the Last Days. The name was later applied to a pair of hills near Cambridge. Local legend claims that a giant who had been rejected in love by the nymph Granta (an early name of the River Cam, which runs through the city) pined away and now lies buried beneath the hills.

---

made him the builder of the Giant's Causeway on the Northern Irish coast and had him living in Fingal's Cave on the Scottish island of Staffa. German folklore told of Rübezahl, a kind-hearted giant living in the Giant Mountains on the Czech–Polish border, while children in the Basque Country still wait for Olentzero, a gigantic alternative Santa Claus, to bring them gifts on Christmas Eve. The children's writer Roald Dahl used this tradition to create *The* B.F.G. or "Big Friendly Giant", a kindly outsider in a land of unsocialized ogres with names like Fleshlumpeater and Childchewer.

Cyclopes One-eyed race of hulks

Appearance
Apart from their gigantic size, the Cyclopes' most distinctive feature was the single eye in the middle of their foreheads.

Size
Very large. Virgil compared them to tall forest trees, and the Spanish poet Luis de Góngora described them using full-grown pines as walking sticks.

Lifespan
The original Cyclopes were godlike, and so presumably very long-lived. However, they were not immortal – Apollo was able to shoot them down with arrows.

Powers
Great physical strength, revealed in their ability to construct massive buildings. Exceptional skills as metalsmiths.

Habitat
Originally associated with Thrace, then with Crete and Lycia. Later said to inhabit forges deep within volcanic Mt. Etna in Sicily. Polyphemus lived on a Mediterranean island, presumably not far from Djerba off the Tunisian coast, the hypothetical scene of Ulysses' preceding encounter with the lotus-eaters.

When people think of the Cyclopes today they generally remember Polyphemus, tricked in a famous episode from Homer's *Odyssey*. This cannibalistic hulk trapped Ulysses' crew in the lonely cavern where he dwelled, beating out their brains and eating them one by one until Ulysses blinded him by driving a heated stake into his single eye. Yet Polyphemus was at best a degenerate specimen of a once-great race. He was living at a time when the Cyclopes had been reduced to the status of savage shepherds, ignorant of law, agriculture and all the amenities of civilized life.

Armourers to the gods

It was not always so. According to the poet Hesiod, the first three Cyclopes – giants with one eye in the middle of their foreheads – were born of the earth mother Gaia by her son Uranus at the very dawn of creation. Called Brontes ("Thunder"), Steropes ("Lightning") and Arges ("Bright"), they were thrown into Tartarus by their unloving father, only to be freed by Zeus, who persuaded

them to fight alongside the Olympian gods in their war with the Titans (see page 58).

In return for their release, the Cyclopes – already famous smiths – gave Zeus his thunderbolts and Neptune his trident. Having helped the Olympians to victory, they were rewarded with forges under Mount Etna in Sicily, where they fashioned the weapons of the gods. Zeus used one of their bolts to kill Apollo's son Asclepius, who had contravened the divine order by raising dead people to life, and in revenge the sun god shot the giants down with arrows. Their ghosts continue to haunt Etna, causing the rumblings and flashes that still disturb the volcano's crater.

Their immediate progeny were likewise smiths, said to have been the first to work iron. They were also builders, and later generations of Greeks would credit them with the construction of the massive stone walls of Mycenae and Tiryns, actually built by masons of the lost Mycenaean culture.

By the time Homer was writing, legends of the Cyclopes were perhaps being confounded with tales of the Arimaspians, a one-eyed race mentioned by the historian Herodotus as dwelling in the far north; according to Pliny the Elder, they lived "not far from where the North Wind rises, near the cave that bears its name". The Arimaspians were said to be engaged in a constant struggle with the griffins (see page 42), seeking to steal gold from the mines the birds protected. Herodotus, however, expressed incredulity, considering it unlikely there should be people "in all else like other men, but having only one eye".

One-eyed bogeymen of the Far East

Japanese legend also recounted tales of one-eyed creatures. The hitotsume-kozo, however, were considerably smaller than adult humans, being about the size of ten-year-old boys, and were totally bald. Goblin-like creatures, they had none of the awful grandeur of their ancient Greek counterparts and were simply bogeymen whose role in Japanese family life was to scare or amuse impressionable children.

Ghouls & Zombies Demons of the undead

GHOULS
Appearance
Demonic, flesh-eating spirits of Arab folklore.

Size
Sometimes vast, although more often that of the creatures (often hyenas) whose shape they borrow.

Lifespan
Undead.

Powers
The ability to shift shape at will, combined with intense malignity and ferocity.

Habitat
Graveyards and waste places, particularly the Arabian desert.

Few places are more lonely or awful than a graveyard at night. Wandering among the headstones, visitors find themselves in thrall to the presence of the departed spirits they commemorate. In their silent company, boundaries between the living and the dead seem to fade, and it is easy to imagine unearthly feet moving across the hummocked earth and non-human eyes watching through the darkness.

In the Arab lands, the fear such places inspire bred stories of *ghuls* or ghouls, demonic spirits spawned of Iblis, the Muslim Satan. Craving flesh to eat, they haunted the abodes of the deceased, seeking corpses that they could first exhume and then consume. And woe betide those who came upon them in their foul exertions, for they too might end up dead, providing extra rations for the hungry grave-robbers.

By a natural extension, the parallel fears felt by lone travellers wandering the Arabian deserts generated similar stories of evil *jinns* (genies) roaming the vastness in search of human sustenance. Such spirits, it was claimed, could take on human or animal form, often that of the striped hyena that stalks the desert fringes looking for carrion. A chance glimpse of a scavenging animal could cause terror for a nervous voyager, uncertain whether he had encountered a wild animal that would flee from human contact or a supernatural predator who would tirelessly track him down.

"Hungry ghosts" and "stiff corpses"

Similar fears found slightly different expression in other cultures. The Japanese told stories of the *nukekubi*, monsters in the guise of human beings whose heads detached at night and flew off in search of human prey. They also spoke of a class of *rakshasa* ("hungry ghosts") known as the *jikininki*, accursed spirits condemned after death to scavenge corpses or the food offerings left out in cemeteries for the dead. The *jikininki* were usually described as corpse-like in appearance, although some were said to be able to disguise themselves as normal mortals during daylight hours.

The nearest Chinese equivalent to the *jikininki* were the *jiang shi*, literally "stiff corpses". These were undead beings who, having committed suicide or never having been properly interred, were fated to hop about in search of living creatures whose *qi* or life essence they could drain. In recent times they became something of a staple of Hong Kong popular culture, featuring in manga comics and horror films where, zombie-like, they were generally shown with fixed expressions and outstretched arms, their upper bodies still apparently gripped by rigor mortis.

Some commentators have speculated that stories of hopping corpses may have been inspired by the Chinese custom of transporting the bodies of dead migrant

> "Craving flesh to eat, they haunted the abodes of the deceased, seeking corpses that they could first exhume and then consume."

labourers back to their home provinces for burial. In times past the corpses were carried on bamboo stretchers where they lay exposed for all to see; viewed from a distance, they sometimes appeared to bounce up and down as the rods flexed beneath them. More cynically, other observers claimed that stories of *jiang shi* were deliberately spread by smugglers to scare away customs officials who might otherwise have disrupted their traffic.

In the Philippines children shuddered at tales of aswangs. Ordinary citizens as it seemed, these necrophages would in fact roam city streets after dark in search of fresh corpses to steal and eat. Failing to find their favoured food,

65

ZOMBIES

Appearance
Corpselike, as befits reanimated dead bodies.

Size
Human.

Lifespan
More of a half-life, as zombies remain dead in spirit. Supposed real-life zombies have returned from the grave after anything from a few days up to 30 years.

Powers
Limited. Having no will of their own, they can only follow the directions of the sorcerer who controls them.

Habitat
Primarily Haiti, although also anywhere where the voudou religion is practised.

aswangs sometimes compromised by eating children, particularly relishing the liver and the heart. Credulous citizens paid careful attention to strangers they passed at night, giving particular heed to their lower limbs, for aswangs' feet were said to face backwards.

Similar stories were once told in England. In the eleventh and twelfth centuries, sober chroniclers living in monasteries passed on reports of the living dead roaming their own country parishes. William of Newborough told of a newly deceased criminal who rose each night from his grave near York to spread terror in the surrounding hamlets. When his tomb was opened, the body was found to be swollen with the blood of many people. Local youths

dealt with the problem by burning the corpse, having first torn out the heart.

Abbot Thomas Burton had a story of two fugitive peasants in southern Yorkshire who, when dead and buried, disturbed their neighbours by wandering around with their coffins on their shoulders, sometimes shape-shifting into the form of dogs or bears. Villagers finally stopped their excursions by exhuming their bodies, cutting off the heads and, again, removing the hearts.

Reanimated corpses of Haiti

Zombies come from African tradition, as transplanted across the Atlantic Ocean to Haiti. A sizeable proportion of the island's population long held the view that sorcerers known as *bokors* had

---

VISITORS FROM VALHALLA

Medieval chroniclers' accounts of bloodthirsty revenants roaming eastern England may have reflected the influence of Norse accounts of draugs. These were the ghosts of Viking warriors who emerged from the grave as reanimated corpses to visit their former haunts as walking dead. As such, they possessed great strength and also sometimes knowledge of the future, but were consumed by a bitter resentment of the living world that they had left behind. They were creatures of the night, and moved around most freely in the winter months when the hours of darkness were longest, often driven by a gnawing hunger that could only be satisfied by the taste of live flesh.

The Old Norse sagas preserved several accounts of heroes grappling with draugs, who could apparently only be subdued in hand-to-hand combat. Once overcome, they had to be decapitated to render them harmless; the corpse was then burned and the ashes thrown into the sea. Only then might the restless dead at last find peace.

the power to reanimate corpses. These creatures had no mind of their own and were simply the tools of their creators.

Such stories may have had some basis in fact. There is evidence that *bokors* used so-called "voodoo dust" containing substances that could temporarily incapacitate a human. The Canadian ethnobotanist Wade Davis, who investigated the phenomenon in the 1980s, identified three such ingredients, derived respectively from a marine toad, a hyla tree frog and, most interestingly, from the puffer fish. These fish are a source of tetrodotoxin, a deadly neural agent. Davis claimed that, when given in a tiny dose, the substance could paralyze a person for several days while leaving him or her still conscious – a condition similar to that described by victims of zombification. One such, Clairvius Narcisse, was supposedly put into a near-death condition in 1962. His *bokor* subsequently kept him subjugated for two years by feeding him a paste containing the hallucinogen datura. During that time he worked for his master on a sugar plantation.

Whatever its real-life justification, the zombie phenomenon has proved big box-office in cinema releases of recent decades. The breakthrough came with George Romero's 1968 horror classic, *Night of the Living Dead*, whose eponymous protagonists combined the mindlessness of zombies with the cannibalistic tastes of ghouls. The subsequent raft of sequels has now even produced an effective parody in the 2004 comedy hit *Shaun of the Dead* – a sure mark of distinction in popular culture.

Hellhounds Black Shuck and other demon dogs

Appearance
Ferocious black dogs, usually large and shaggy, with slavering mouths and flaming eyes. Occasionally headless. May drag chains or smell of sulphur.

Size
Typically described as calf-sized, although some are as big as bullocks. Others are no larger than a retriever.

Lifespan
Supernatural, and so unlimited.

Powers
The ability to foretell death and disaster.

Habitat
Lonely tracks and dark places. Also cemeteries and other sites associated with death.

Alone on the moor at night, a traveller hears a distant howling that gradually draws closer through the darkness. Frantically he peers into the mist swirling about him, seeking to know the direction from which the creature is approaching. Then suddenly it is upon him, huge and black, its fangs bared and its eyes glowing with a baleful, infernal light …

Sir Arthur Conan Doyle imagined this chilling scene for the classic Sherlock Holmes mystery, *The Hound of the Baskervilles*, but it drew on a long tradition of British folklore. Stories of supernatural black dogs and spectral hounds crop up in many parts of the United Kingdom. Examples include the barghest of Yorkshire, the *moddey dhoo* ("black dog" in Manx) of the Isle of Man, and East Anglia's Black Shuck. There are also regional differences, notably the *cu sith* or "fairy hound" of the Scottish Highlands which, unusually, is dark green.

The best known of the animals is probably Black Shuck, although analysis of the many stories that have grown up around it show little consistency in the telling. Sometimes the dog is threatening, at other times an almost friendly presence. Often it appears or disappears mysteriously, sometimes vanishing into thin air, but on other occasions it simply lopes away. Some witnesses are convinced of its supernatural origins by its unnatural size, others because of its fiery eyes or the fact that it disappears inexplicably.

"A Strange and Terrible Wonder"
Yet Black Shuck has at least one ancient written source for its hellhound pedigree. On August 4, 1577 a terrible storm struck the county of Suffolk, sweeping through the town of Bungay and striking down the steeple of Blythburgh Church, a well-known landmark. Soon after the event a pamphlet appeared entitled *A Strange and Terrible Wonder wrought very Lately in the Parish Church of Bungay*. Written by a London clergyman named Abraham Fleming, it claimed that the storm had been accompanied by the appearance of a supernatural black dog, which broke

into Bungay Church and attacked two of the parishioners as they knelt praying, snapping their necks. It then turned its attention to a third man, giving him "such a grip on the back that therewithal he was presently drawn together and shrunk up, as if he were a piece of leather scorched in a hot fire; or as the mouth of a purse or bag, drawn together with string". This victim survived the assault, "which thing is marvellous in the eyes of men". The dog then made its way to Blythburgh Church, more than ten miles away, and repeated the performance: "There also, as before, [it] slew two men and a lad, and burned the hand

"Among other charges brought against him, Cade was accused of having 'raised up the Devil in the semblance of a black dog' at Dartford in his home county of Kent."

of another person that was there among the rest of the company, of whom divers were blasted".

Harbingers of doom

Fleming's account seems to be unique in describing a murderous assault by a black dog. Usually they were seen as portents of doom rather than active agents of destruction – a tradition that Conan Doyle also drew on to invent the curse of the Baskervilles. A real-life parallel involved the Vaughn family of the Welsh border marches, who were supposed to regularly see a black dog before a member of the family died. One account of its coming told how a husband kept the story from his wife until one of their children fell ill of smallpox. The wife went upstairs to check on the invalid as the family were about to sit down to dinner, only to rush down again moments later saying that a large black dog was lying on the child's

bed. Fearing the worst, the husband ran to the bedroom, where he found the dog gone and the child already dead.

Such stories go back a long way, to judge from a reference in Plutarch's life of the Athenian statesman Cimon; the Greek biographer recorded that a black dog appeared as a harbinger of the general's death. The beasts' role as doom-bringers may partly explain the linguistic tradition linking them with melancholia. Sir Winston Churchill famously used the phrase "black dog" to describe the bouts of depression that periodically afflicted him throughout his career. Churchill borrowed the phrase from the eighteenth-century man of letters Dr Samuel Johnson, a fellow sufferer. Johnson in turn was echoing a traditional saying reserved for sulky children or disconsolate adults, that they "had a black dog on their back".

Hellhound on my trail

The idea of the dog as a messenger of fate combined with the image of a bloodhound tracking down its prey to create the imagery of Robert Johnson's famous 1930s blues song, *Hellhound on My Trail*: "I got to keep movin'/Blues fallin' down like hail/And the days keep on worryin' me/There's a hellhound on my trail". Forty years earlier, the opium-addicted

English poet Francis Thompson had inverted the image to write *The Hound of Heaven*, describing how God pursued his soul through all the travails of a wasted and unhappy life.

Mythographers seeking to trace the origins of the hellhound legends have struggled to find a single agreed source. One strand of research traces the idea to Cerberus, the three-headed guardian of the Greco-Roman underworld, or to Garm, his Norse equivalent. Another line of enquiry stretches back into the lore of witchcraft, in which dogs sometimes replaced the more common cats as witches' familiars. The earliest known reference to a hellhound in England dates from the arrest warrant issued for Jack Cade, leader of a popular revolt against the government of King Henry VI in 1450. Among other charges brought against him, Cade was accused of having "raised up the Devil in the semblance of a black dog" at Dartford in his home county of Kent.

Whatever its origins, the concept of a hound of fate presaging evil fortune became entrenched, not just in Britain but also across much of Europe and North America; the Catalans for one have a demon dog called Dip, lame in one leg, that sucks people's blood. Maybe such stories serve a necessary psychic function, expressing suppressed fears of the fiercer aspect of the animal most people view as man's best friend.

THE WILD HUNT

In northern Europe in past centuries, people seeing a sudden storm sweep across the sky would say that the Wild Hunt was passing. The allusion was to a long-held belief that spectral huntsmen sometimes coursed through the heavens, pursuing unseen prey to the accompaniment of hunting horns and the baying of phantom hounds. As with the black dog of British folklore, the sight of the wild hunt was considered ominous, presaging either disaster or the death of the individual who happened to see it.

The legend was always most firmly rooted in Germany, and its origins have been traced back to Germanic myth – initially the huntsman was the god Woden or Odin. Similar beliefs in Britain, where the hunting dogs were sometimes referred to as Gabriel's Hounds, may have reflected a separate, Celtic tradition. Welsh legend told of the hounds of Arawn, ruler of the magical underworld realm of Annwn, who sometimes ventured into the mortal world in pursuit of game. There the fairy beasts could be easily recognized by their distinctive white coats and red ears.

Household Spirits Impish presences in the home

Appearance
Typically tiny, elderly men with full beards dressed in peasants' clothing. Brownies often had a brownish hue, or wore a hooded brown cloak. The domovoi was generally shaggy, sometimes covered all over in hair.

Size
Small, ranging from a few inches up to about 3ft (1m).

Lifespan
Longer than human.

Powers
Immense strength despite their small stature. Some had shape-shifting powers. Ability to foretell the future.

Habitat
Homes and farmyards across northern Europe, including Scandinavia and the Slavic lands.

One of the best loved of the Grimm Brothers' tales concerns an impoverished shoemaker who puts out his last pieces of leather on his workbench one night, only to find them converted the next morning into a fine pair of shoes. He sells the shoes for a handsome price that enables him to buy more leather, which is again nocturnally transformed, this time into two pairs – a process that continues night after night until his fortunes are restored.

Eventually he and his wife stay up one night to find the identity of their secret helpers. They turn out to be a couple of small, bearded figures who work with wonderful dexterity, taking care to complete their work and vanish before dawn. Eager to thank them, the wife makes each one a set of clothes, laying them out the next evening alongside the shoe leather. Later that night, the couple watch as the tiny men try on their new outfits in glee, only to then disappear from the house forever, their job accomplished.

The English version of the story commonly goes under the title of *The Elves and the Shoemaker*, but to folklorists the creatures are unmistakably boggarts – household spirits that go under many different names in different lands. "Boggarts" is specifically northern English; the Scottish equivalents are brownies. In Shakespeare's day the unseen housemates, by turn helpful or mischievous, were addressed as Puck, or alternately as Robin Goodfellow. Sweden has its tomte – short for *tomt-gubbe*, "old man of the house" – and Denmark and Norway the nisse. The Germanic version was the kobold, and in the Slav lands there were the domovoi, whose origins have been traced back to ancestral spirits presiding over the family home from a preferred spot behind or beneath the stove.

Rewards for the deserving

The household spirits shared much in common, although there were some regional differences. They could be helpful or harmful, largely depending on how they themselves were treated. They liked clean, well-tended homes where everything was customary, and tended to punish slovenliness, bad language and mistreatment of animals. They kept to themselves and did not like to be seen, only coming out in the hours when the rest of the household was sleeping – and not always then, to judge from the Lancashire rhyme: "Stars is shining/Moon is bright/Boggart won't come out tonight". They also had a particular aversion to being mentioned by name; Russian families took care to refer to

> "They liked clean, well-tended homes where everything was customary, and tended to punish slovenliness, bad language and mistreatment of animals."

their domovoi in the third person, as "he" or "himself" or else as "grandfather".

On the other hand, the spirits appreciated gifts, particularly of food, and wise householders would leave small offerings of bread or milk by the hearth at night. It was a mistake to give them clothes, however, or else they tended to decamp, as in the story of the Elves and the Shoemaker. A Scottish rhyme summed up this point: "A new cloak, a new hood/Brownie will do no more good".

Families who treated their boggarts in a benign and generous way would receive many small favours in return: the spirits might tidy the house, return lost objects, even braid the tails of horses in the stables, for they were found on every farm. One well-known Scottish story told how a brownie who had been ministered to by a kindly housewife took dramatic action to protect her when she

THE IRISH POOKA

Sometimes claimed as the origin of Shakespeare's Puck, the "shrewd and knavish sprite" of A *Midsummer Night's Dream*, Ireland's pooka was a solitary fairy that combined shape-shifting powers with classic features of the domestic spirit. Unlike boggarts or brownies, however, he normally lived outside, haunting waste places and ruins. Yet pookas sometimes came indoors, as a story from Kildare suggested. It recounted how a scullion who fell asleep in the hearth of a big-house kitchen one night awoke to an extraordinary sight – the spectacle of a large ass busily engaged in doing the housework. The animal left only when the room had been swept spotless. Next morning the rest of the staff were nonplussed by the boy's story but were delighted to find the cleaning done for them, the more so when the same scene was repeated on following nights.

Eventually the strange visitor was persuaded to tell his story. Himself a lazy servant during his time on Earth, he had been condemned after death to take animal form and do all the menial work he had failed to do in his human lifetime. Saddened by the tale, the servants sought to reward the pooka by making him a quilted horse-jacket to keep him warm out of doors, but their kindness proved ill-conceived. In the fashion of boggarts, he accepted the gift with delight and then was seen no more, considering his job done.

---

was taken dangerously ill in the middle of the night. Realizing that nobody in the house was willing to set off through the darkness in search of medical help, he took the initiative, borrowing a horse from the stable to ride to the nearest village. Knowing that his odd appearance might scare off potential helpers, he also took the precaution of disguising himself beneath a long brown cloak. It was only after he had ridden back with the local nurse perched behind him on the saddle that he revealed his true identity – much to the chagrin of the stay-at-home humans who had lacked his resourcefulness and courage.

If good behaviour was rewarded, mistreatment of boggarts courted punishment. Households that failed to observe the necessary courtesies could expect to be afflicted by all the misfortunes associated with minor poltergeist infestations: broken dishes, creaking walls, objects that moved or rattled inexplicably, pinched noses, boxed ears, muddy footprints appearing from nowhere in the middle of the living-room floor. More serious transgressions tended to be punished more severely: cattle might be released from the byre at night or even killed, or the house itself set on fire.

74

The Boggart's Flitting

The well-known northern story of the Boggart's Flitting neatly caught the ambivalent feelings people had about their unseen companions. It told of a family that was driven to distraction by the ministrations of a mischievous boggart until finally they decided they could stand no more. The father piled all the household belongings onto a cart and was about to set out in search of a new home, when a neighbour called by to ask why they were leaving. Bitterly the man enumerated all the petty miseries to which the household had been subjected. Then, just as he was coming to an end, a small, unfamiliar voice from somewhere near the top of the pile added helpfully, "So you see, Geordie, we're flitting!" The family took the point and stayed put, realizing that they would simply have to live with the boggart if there was to be no escaping from him. In Russia, sensible householders took care to keep the domovoi in mind when moving house, providing an old shoe for him to hide in for the journey and taking a brand from the stove to make him feel at ease in the new home.

A modern-day Goodfellow

In recent times household spirits have faded from prominence, but they still have a place in popular culture. Brownies are now best known in English-speaking countries as the junior branch of the Girl Guides, while "to boggart" is a dialect term meaning to take more than one's fair share. The sprites have also taken on a new incarnation as the house elves of the Harry Potter books; the sad, bat-eared Dobby is in effect Robin Goodfellow for a new generation.

HONOURING THE HOUSEHOLD GODS

The tradition of paying respect to presiding spirits of the household goes back to classical times. Roman citizens took care to propitiate the *lares* – spirits of departed ancestors – and the *penates*, originally gods of the *penus*, or store-cupboard, whose job it was to see that the family always had food to put on the table. The two sets of guardians were worshipped at a small shrine set up conspicuously in the living room, supporting their effigies in metal or clay. The head of the household would say a prayer at the altar each day, and the family would regularly leave small offerings of wine or incense.

Amphisbaena Serpent with two heads

Appearance
A snake or lizard with heads at both ends of its body. Sometimes shown, dragonlike, with scaled feet and wings; also occasionally with horns or ears.

Size
Medium-sized snake, about 3 feet (1m) long.

Lifespan
Unspecified. Modern Amphisbaenidae generally live in captivity for 1 to 2 years.

Powers
Speedy movement forward or backward, either by slithering or rolling. Venomous fangs. The ability to regenerate itself if cut in two.

Habitat
The Libyan desert.

In the second century BCE the Greek poet Nicander wrote a poem on the subject of venomous beasts. One of the creatures he described was a snake called the amphisbaena, a word that means "goes both ways". The name was apt for, according to the poet, the creature had heads at both ends of its body.

In the first century CE the Roman naturalist Pliny the Elder expanded on his claims, noting that "the amphisbaena has a twin head, in other words one at the tail as well, as if one mouth were not enough to pour out poison". Other classical writers also mentioned the creature, notably the poet Lucan, who in his epic *Pharsalia* included it in a list of serpents that assailed Cato's forces on their march through Libya during the civil war against Julius Caesar. All of these beasts, according to Lucan, were born of drops of the Gorgon Medusa's blood that had fallen in the desert when the hero Perseus flew over it carrying her decapitated head.

Stories of the amphisbaena were taken up enthusiastically by the writers of the medieval bestiaries. According to

Isidore of Seville, writing in the sixth century, it was warm-blooded: "It is the only serpent that exposes itself to the cold, showing itself before any of the others". Other writers gave it wings and scaled feet, turning it into a two-headed dragon. It appeared in this form in several medieval manuscript illuminations, and also was used in church decoration – for example in Limerick Cathedral in Ireland. Some illustrators portrayed it looped into a hoop with one head clutched in the jaws of the other, implying that it could roll as well as slither.

Putting the venom to use

The classical writers had already specified some of the medicinal properties of the amphisbaena. A work attributed to the Greek physician Galen claimed that, while alive, it exuded a noxious vapour that could cause pregnant women to abort if they happened unknowingly to step over one. Amphisbaena skins, however, were thought to have a variety of therapeutic uses. Nicander himself suggested that they could counteract the effects of cold if wrapped tightly around a stick. Such wands also had the advantage of scaring away other venomous animals.

The seventeenth-century sceptic Sir Thomas Browne questioned the amphisbaena's existence, along with that of many other mythical beasts, in his 1646 work *Vulgar Errors*. In particular he cited the philosophical difficulty of having a creature with two sets of foreparts and no hindparts – in his view, a physiological impossibility.

From Browne's day on, belief in the double-headed snake gradually faded. Yet in one sense the amphisbaena had the last laugh. Modern zoologists chose to apply its name to a group of limbless, burrowing subtropical reptiles, known as the worm-lizards. So now, in scientific textbooks, there is a suborder of Amphisbaenia and, within it, a family of Amphisbaenidae – but, contrary to legend, the creatures that comprise it each have only a single head.

Lamia   Cannibalistic temptress

Appearance
A beautiful woman in her head and upper body, but a snake from the waist down.

Size
Human-sized.

Lifespan
Immortal.

Powers
A cannibalistic appetite for eating other women's children. Drains the life force from the men whom she seduces. The ability to remove and replace her own eyes at will.

Habitat
Initially Libya, but in modern Greek and Bulgarian folklore associated with caves and dank places underground.

Originally, Lamia was a character from Greek myth. The daughter of Belus, king of Egypt, she ruled over Libya, where her beauty attracted the attention of the mighty Zeus himself. In return for her favours, the king of the gods gave her the ability to pluck out and replace her own eyes – a symbol of prophecy or "second sight", for the myths also claimed that she was the mother of the Libyan Sibyl, who presided over the oracle of Zeus Ammon in the Siwa Oasis.

Lamia bore Zeus several other children, and these attracted the jealousy of his wife Hera. The angry goddess killed them all, but for one other daughter, Scylla, whom she transformed into a six-headed monster (see pages 204–205).

Driven mad by grief, Lamia herself became morally monstrous, her entire life devoted to revenge. She sought

THE LETHAL LILITH

Lilith was the deadly seductress of Hebrew legend, later identified, in the Middle Ages, as the mother of the incubi and succubi, demons that seduced individuals in their sleep (see page 180). Lilith's origins lay in early Mesopotamian myth – a female storm-demon named Lilitu is mentioned in the *Epic of Gilgamesh*. The same creature gets a mention in the biblical Book of Isaiah, where the prophet claims of the foreseen destruction of Edom that "Yea, there shall Lilith alight, and find for herself a resting-place". In modern translations, Lilith is often rendered as "the night-hag", for ancient tradition identified her as a monstrous creature who travelled by night, killing infants and pregnant mothers; as such, she became associated with owls, which served as her familiars.

Another line of thought identified her as Adam's first wife, made when God originally created man and woman – an action that, in the Genesis account, predated the creation of Eve from Adam's rib. This Lilith had strong sexual connotations, being identified with prostitutes – one Talmudic text said of her that "she wanders about at night, vexing the sons of men and causing them to defile themselves". In popular culture she subsequently became a symbol of the *femme fatale* or seductress – and, in a recent ironic twist, something of a feminist icon.

to inflict the anguish she had suffered on other mothers by stealing and eating their infant children. She also joined forces with the Empusae, night-hags who sometimes took the form of lovely women to seduce young men, sucking the life force from them until they died.

Both activities justified Lamia's name, which derived from *lamyros*, Greek for "gluttonous". In later folklore she came to be regarded as a greedy slattern whose slovenliness was proverbial – a nightmare creature who haunted caves and hidden places, and was held responsible for sudden infant deaths. For children she was a much-feared bogeywoman.

Tender prey

Yet a more romantic tradition also survived, portraying her instead as a hybrid temptress – an alluring woman from the waist up who went to great lengths to conceal the fact that her lower body was that of a serpent. John Keats drew on this image in his long poem *Lamia*, although he chose to present her as an attractive girl magically trapped within the body of a serpent. More recently Peter Gabriel, then of the rock group Genesis, revived the erotic connotations of the legend in his song "The Lamia", written for the band's 1974 rock opera *The Lamb Lies Down on Broadway*. His lamiae are snakes with women's faces who tenderly devour their human lovers.

Minotaur Half-bull, half-human

Appearance
Hybrid creature with a bull's head on the body of a man (although the Italian poet Dante pictured it in the *Inferno* with a man's head on a bull's body).

Size
Slightly larger than human, fleshed out with taurine muscular bulk.

Lifespan
Probably 20 to 30 years. The creature consumed its tribute of Athenian youths and maidens once every 9 years; its killer Theseus volunteered to form part of the third consignment.

Powers
Great physical strength fuelled by an appetite for human flesh.

Habitat
The Labyrinth – a subterranean maze built by the engineer and inventor Daedalus under King Minos's palace in Knossos, Crete.

The legend of the Minotaur, half-bull and half-human, has enthralled countless generations since it surfaced in classical Greece more than two millennia ago. The story tells how Pasiphae, wife of King Minos of Crete, conceived an unnatural passion for a white bull that emerged from the sea, sent by the god Poseidon. Her aberrant liaison with the bull resulted in the Minotaur. Being sacred to Poseidon it could not be killed, and so it was hidden away in the Labyrinth, devised by the inventor Daedalus under the palace at Knossos.

But the beast craved human flesh, and to feed it Minos – the ruler of a seaborne empire – demanded a tribute of seven youths and seven maidens from Athens on the Greek mainland. This ghastly arrangement endured until Theseus, an Athenian hero, determined to put an end to it. He volunteered to make the trip, and once on Crete secured the aid, and the heart, of Minos's own daughter Ariadne, who gave him a ball of twine to mark his passage through the maze. In its depths he encountered the beast and killed it. He then followed the twine back to the Labyrinth's entrance, and he and his comrades escaped by ship back to Athens, inexplicably abandoning Ariadne on Naxos along the way.

Modern scholars hypothesize that the story drew on memories of the great Cretan civilization that flourished long ago. Excavations have shown that the palace at Knossos was indeed labyrinthine in its groundplan, and frescoes found on its walls show that young people there took part in bull-leaping contests – seizing the horns of charging bulls to somersault over their backs. Conceivably the myth even preserved fragments of some ancient ceremonial involving the ritual mating of a king in a bull mask and a high priestess wearing cow's horns, symbolizing the primordial marriage of the Sun and the Moon.

Tupilak Devil-dolls of the Arctic Circle

Appearance
Effigies carved from human or animal body parts.

Size
Often no more than an inch (2.5cm) in length.

Lifespan
An activated tupilak could retain its powers for years.

Powers
The ability to bring death, illness or misfortune on its target unless he or she took ritual counter-measures to avert the threat.

Habitat
The Inuit lands of the Arctic.

Living in one of the world's harshest environments, the Inuit of the Arctic also inhabited a universe alive with spirits. Some were benevolent and others malign, but all were creatures of power that required careful handling. To avoid giving offence by neglecting necessary rituals or breaking taboos, people turned to shamans who were specialists in dealings with the spirit world.

The shamans, known as *angakuit*, mostly worked within the community to heal sickness, tend wounds or summon game in times of hunger. But some rogue *angakuit* also sought to work harm on their enemies. Their tools were tupilaks – small effigies formed from bone, peat and cloth, sometimes including human hair or other body parts. The tupilaks were grotesque little devil-dolls with grimacing faces and staring eyes. Some were fashioned to resemble seals or walruses or polar bears.

In themselves the tupilaks had no power until their creator brought them to life. To activate the figure the *angakok*

THE GOLEM

Jewish legend also spoke of an artificial creature that could be brought to life, in its case to protect ghetto communities against anti-semitic attacks. The stories claimed that the sixteenth-century rabbi Judah Loew – a real-life figure famed for his scholarship and mystical interests – created the golem in Prague from clay taken from the banks of the Vltava River. Just as God gave life to Adam, so the rabbi animated his creation by chanting incantations in Hebrew. But, Frankenstein-like, he soon found that he could not control the monster he had brought to life.

When the golem's depradations got out of hand, the Jews' persecutors begged him to destroy it. Rabbi Loew agreed on condition that mistreatment of his people should stop, and then neutralized the golem simply by rubbing out the "e" of the word *emet* ("truth") inscribed on its forehead. The erasure left the word *met*, Hebrew for "death". Some say, though, that the golem is not so much dead as in suspended animation; it lives on in a Prague attic, waiting to be resuscitated at some future time if its services should ever again be needed.

would sing a song or chant a magic formula. Working alone and in the strictest secrecy, he might rub the effigy against his sexual organs, causing it to swell in size. Then he would send it on its way to wreak harm on his enemy, typically by putting it in the sea to "swim" to its victim. The spirit would embody itself in the form that he had given the tupilak, so if he had fashioned the likeness of a seal, an apparently flesh-and-blood seal would be the instrument of his vengeance.

Taking protective measures

Many Inuit tales recounted the fate of individuals who were targeted by tupilaks. Not all ended in disaster, for a canny target, well-versed in shamanistic lore, could use his skill either to evade the threat or even to turn the tupilak's destructive power on the *angakok* who had created it.

One story told of two hunters who encountered a tupilak in the form of a seal. Sensing a warm glow in his belly – a sure sign of approaching psychic danger – the first hunter reached for a

wolf's muzzle amulet he was carrying and rubbed his midriff with it to neutralize the force directed against him. His companion was not so lucky. He shot the seal, which disappeared beneath the water's surface, leaving him with a burning sensation in his stomach. A few moments later blood started gushing from his mouth, and he died soon after.

Tupilaks' ability to do harm rested in the fear they inspired and the belief people had in them. Today both have waned, and the effigies are now carved as souvenirs for the tourist trade, their murderous powers gone and their spiritual force neutered.

Dwarf An underground race of miners and craftsmen

Appearance
Short and stocky, with dark skin, powerful physique, and long beard (in some traditions, even the womenfolk were bearded). Sometimes said to have flat feet or even feet facing backward, giving them a clumsy gait.

Size
Usually described as being between 2 feet and 3 feet tall (0.6–1m).

Lifespan
Opinions vary. Some folk traditions claimed a dwarf was fully grown at age three and an old man at seven. But the dwarves (sic) of J.R.R. Tolkien's *Lord of the Rings* trilogy lived for four times the normal human span – upward of 250 years.

Powers
Great physical strength combined with a canny mindset and phenomenal skill in mining and, above all, metalwork.

Habitat
Underground or in mountain regions in northern parts of Europe.

The dwarfs of legend are not simply small people. They belong to a separate race, whose origins can be traced back to Norse myth. This describes how they were spontaneously generated as maggots on the body of the primordial earth-giant Ymir. The gods then gave them consciousness and intelligence greater than that granted to humans.

Thereafter they lived in the underground realm of Nidavellir, working as miners and metalworkers. They were fabulously wealthy, having a particular liking for gold. But they were also inspired craftsmen who could create objects of dazzling power and beauty.

Making gifts for the gods

Most stories about the dwarfs in the myths involved their wonderful creations. For the god Freyr they fashioned a ship, Skidbladnir, that always commanded a fair wind and that conveniently could be folded away when not in use and carried in a pouch. Freyr also received the boar Gullinbursti ("Golden Bristles"), which glowed in the dark and ran faster than any horse. When the

trickster Loki cut off the hair of Thor's wife Sif, Thor forced him to get the dwarfs to make her a new head of hair out of gold – a task they performed so well that the artificial locks subsequently grew as naturally as the real ones they replaced. Famed weapon-makers, the dwarfs crafted Odin's spear Gungnir, which never missed its target, and Thor's hammer Mjollnir, which returned to his hand whenever it was thrown.

The myths also credited the dwarfs with a powerful libido. When the goddess Freya demanded to own the glorious necklace of the Brisings, the four dwarfs who had made it named as the price that she should sleep with each of them in turn. Freya duly paid up.

Another story told how the dwarf Alviss – the name means "all wise" – agreed to provide weapons for the gods in return for Thor's daughter Thrud in marriage. Thor himself had no part in the deal, and when he heard of it he immediately determined to quash the match. Meeting Alviss that night on his way back from Asgard, the home of the gods, he challenged him to a contest of wits, promising to give his consent if the dwarf could answer the riddles he posed. Confident of his abilities, Alviss agreed and correctly solved all the problems the god threw at him. But Thor had a plan. He knew that the dwarfs, as subterranean beings, could not stand daylight, so he kept on putting questions until the first streak of dawn spread across the sky, whereupon Alviss was turned to stone, and Thrud was freed from the betrothal.

Andvari's curse

Perhaps as a result of such treatment, the dwarfs could be suspicious, and sometimes malign. They fashioned caps and cloaks for themselves that could make them invisible, so they could spy on gods and humans. They also learned to project their magic into the future in the form of curses, thereby setting off a saga of misfortunes that was to become one of the best known of all Germanic legends.

The tale told how the mischievous Loki used a net to catch a very wealthy dwarf named Andvari. Loki would only agree to ransom him in return not just for his gold but also for Andvarinaut, the magic ring he had used to make it. The dwarf had no option but to comply, but in doing so he cursed the ring and all who should come

to possess it. Thereafter the ring brought destruction on a succession of owners – the dwarf king Hreidmar, his son Fafnir (see page 167), the hero Sigurd, his beloved Brunnehilde. The composer

> "They might lend a hand in the fields, for which they expected to be rewarded with a piece of cake or some other tidbit laid out overnight on the blade of a plough."

Richard Wagner used the story as the basis of the *Ring* opera cycle.

With the coming of Christianity to the northern lands, the dwarfs receded into folklore. Many of the old beliefs about them survived, although in a less systematic form. They were still thought of as living underground – in splendid palaces, it was said. The men continued to be smiths and miners, although now they had wives who were skilled at spinning and weaving. They retained the power to become invisible, and could also shift shape – they were thought to turn themselves into toads if they wanted to go out in daytime. At night they could emerge in their own guise, and loved feasting and dancing under the full moon.

The dwarfs of medieval Germany and Scandinavia had an ambivalent relationship with humans, sometimes helping and sometimes hindering them in their daily affairs. Occasionally they were accused of theft when objects went missing, and in rare cases they were even blamed for the abduction of women or children. They were also known to take revenge on anyone who crossed them. But those who treated them respectfully could usually count on their good will. They might lend a hand in the fields, for which they expected to be rewarded

THE MINING KOBOLDS

Germany had its own tradition of underground mining folk. Called kobolds like the household spirits of the same name (see page 73), they were in fact a distinct race, inhabiting mines rather than people's homes. In character they tended to the darker end of the kobold spectrum, being for the most part regarded as malicious tricksters who were blamed for anything that went wrong in the shafts. The mineral cobalt was named for them in this spirit, for the ore was at first regarded as simply a poor substitute for silver, switched by the kobolds to frustrate miners' hopes. In 1548 the great German mineralogist Georgius Agricola devoted a whole book, *De animantibus subterraneis* ("Of Subterranean Beings"), to the kobolds and their doings.

with a piece of cake or some other tidbit laid out overnight on the blade of a plough. There were people who claimed to have met them, and in such cases they proferred good advice, for they could see into the future. In some stories they gave presents – a great boon, for their gifts generally turned to gold in the recipient's hands.

Gathering berries in winter

These kinder, gentler dwarfs turn up in various folk tales, of which the story of Snow White is the best known. The Grimm Brothers collected a similar narrative about a cruel wife who sent out her stepdaughter in a paper dress in the depths of winter in search of strawberries, telling her not to return until she had picked a basketful. Shivering and disconsolate, the girl found her way to a small hut deep in the forest where three dwarfs lived. There she happily shared her single crust of bread with them, and in return was rewarded, not just with the strawberries she needed but also with three gifts: she would become more beautiful each day, marry a king, and drop a piece of gold from her mouth each time she spoke. When the stepmother's own daughter subsequently tried to repeat the feat, she made the mistake of speaking harshly to the dwarfs and

THE GREEN CHILDREN

Two English medieval chroniclers, Ralph of Coggeshall and William of Newborough, told a curious story of two children, a boy and a girl, who emerged from underground into twelfth-century East Anglia. Their skin had a greenish tinge and they spoke a language that the local people could not understand. They survived for some time on nothing but beans. The boy pined away and died, but the girl gradually adapted to her new circumstances, learning to speak English, broadening her diet, and accepting baptism. She claimed to have come from a land of perpetual twilight, where she and her brother had been tending sheep when they happened upon a cavern. Following through it, they had been attracted by the sound of church bells, and so had found their way to the place where they had been discovered. The girl is said to have gradually lost her green hue and to have married and settled down in her new home.

refusing to share her bread. As a result, she was condemned to grow daily uglier and eventually die a cruel death, while each time she opened her mouth a toad emerged in place of treasure.

By the twentieth century such tales had mostly lost their grittier qualities. The Dvalin, Skirfir and Hor of Norse myth had been replaced by Disney's Doc, Sneezy and Happy. It took Tolkien's *Lord of the Rings* to restore to the dwarf race something of the epic dignity of its past. Sturdy, axe-wielding warriors, his dwarves (a plural form that he himself coined) were far closer in spirit to the inhabitants of Nidavellir than the whimsical beings of the intervening years.

⊙ ⊕ ⊖

Elf Fair creatures from the realm of light

88

Appearance
"Fairer than the sun", according to the *Prose Edda*. The Anglo-Saxons had a saying, "as lovely as an elf".

Size
Human-sized in Norse myth, they shrank in later legend to tiny beings sometimes smaller than sparrows.

Lifespan
Exceptionally long-lived, when not immortal.

Powers
Skilled in magic and in foresight. Themselves free from the ravages of age, they could also make time slow or stop for human visitors to Elfland.

Habitat
The light elves of Nordic myth lived in Alfheim, a division of Asgard, the realm of the gods. Later legend associated them with woods and hills or mounds.

Elves trace their origins back to Norse myth. The *Prose Edda*, a key text, says, when describing the various realms of Asgard, the home of the gods, that: "one is called Alfheim, where the people called light elves live; but the dark elves dwell down in the earth and are totally different in appearance and even more so in nature. For the light elves are fairer to look upon than the Sun, while the dark elves are blacker than pitch." Subsequent references make it clear that for Snorri Sturluson, the author of the *Edda*, the dark elves were synonymous with the dwarfs (see pages 84–87).

Unlike the dwarfish smiths and miners, the light elves were seen as intermediaries between the human and divine worlds. As such, they came under the protection of Freyr, the lord of Alfheim. When they visited Midgard, home of the human race, they sometimes served as Norns, the supernatural beings who attended babies at birth and helped shape their destiny. The children who entered the world with an elf as their protector were lucky indeed, for their futures were assured.

Those not so fortunate sometimes sought help from elves by offering them sacrifices; one saga relates how a hero was instructed to kill a bull on an elf-hill to speed recovery from a battle wound. Similar practices survived until the very end of the pagan era, to judge from a tenth-century poem in which the author, a Christian, complains of being denied access to a pagan household because an *alfblot* or elf-sacrifice was being performed within.

With the end of paganism, elves shrank into folklore. Physically they diminished from the human-sized creatures of Norse myth to the diminutive beings beloved of Victorian illustrators. They then became confused with other small peoples: in Germany they became

"They were thought of as beautiful maidens inhabiting hills or woods, where they might be seen dancing by night or on misty mornings."

almost indistinguishable from kobolds, as suggested by the tale of *The Elves and the Shoemaker* (see page 72), while in Shakespeare's England they were virtually the same as fairies. Only in Scandinavia did they retain something of their former dignity. There they were thought of as beautiful maidens inhabiting hills or woods, where they might be seen dancing by night or on misty mornings. Something of the *alfblot* tradition survived too in the habit of making small offerings, typically of milk or honey, to win their favour.

Yet even outside the old Norse lands some elements of past beliefs lingered. In English lore elves were credited with making mischief. An unexplained tangle of hair on a person or an animal was called an elf-lock, while a sudden stitch, or an unexpected illness in livestock, might be blamed on an elf-bolt or elf-shot. Usually these elfin weapons were invisible, but some people pointed to Stone Age arrowheads as evidence of their material reality. Meanwhile, will-o'-the-wisps were known as elf-lights, and smooth depressions on boulders were elf-cups.

By the twentieth century such beliefs had faded, and elves were in danger of being relegated to children's picture books, most prominently as Santa's helpers. They were rescued by J.R.R. Tolkien, whose *Lord of the Rings* trilogy successfully reinvented elves for a new generation. In Celeborn, Legolas, Galadriel and their kin, he created worthy successors to the light elves of Nordic legend: beings of human stature but wiser, fairer and less time-worn than the harried race of men.

Fairies An alternative world of ever-youthful beings

Appearance
Varied. The inhabitants of fairyland were beautiful and ageless, spared the ravages of time. Solitary fairies tended to be less glamorous; leprechauns and their ilk were usually gnarled old men.

Size
"Sometimes as big as we are, sometimes bigger, and sometimes, as I have been told, about 3 feet high", according to the poet W.B. Yeats. Modern fairies tend to be smaller, often only inches tall.

Lifespan
In fairyland, eternal – its inhabitants knew neither sickness nor age.

Powers
Magical powers of shape-shifting and enchantment. The ability to fly, to heal people at a touch, and to make wonderful music. Under normal circumstances, invisible to human eyes.

Habitat
All over the world, but especially Ireland and other Celtic lands.

90

In Jorge Luis Borges's words, they were "the most numerous, the most beautiful, and the most memorable of the minor supernatural beings". They were also among the most ubiquitous, for most nations, at least in Europe and Asia, had stories of fairy-like creatures, telling of a race living alongside humankind and interacting with people in unpredictable ways, sometimes kind and sometimes cruel.

In its broadest sense the term "fairy folk" could include gnomes and elves, boggarts and dwarfs. Fairies themselves had diverse roots. The word derived from the Latin *fatum*, meaning "fate", linking them to the three Fates who, in classical mythology, were present at every birth, assigning the new-born infant its destiny. This tradition lingered on in folktales of fairy godmothers.

In Ireland, where fairy lore was particularly well developed, they were traditionally divided into two different lineages: solitary fairies such as leprechauns, and the gregarious trooping fairies. The solitary fairies came in many different varieties. Writing in 1891, the poet W.B. Yeats listed nine of them, including: the banshee (see pages 146–147); the *far darrig* ("red man"), a malicious practical joker; the *far gorta* ("man of hunger"), an emaciated figure who appeared in time of famine; and the dullahan, a headless coachman whose black vehicle was an ominous sign of approaching death.

Two of the other fairies were dangerously malevolent. The beautiful but deadly *leanhaun shee* ("fairy mistress") drained the life from her human lovers, causing them to waste away. As for the pooka (see also page 74), he was a shape-shifter who took animal form as a horse, bull or goat to plague drunkards. If he could get one up on his back, he would carry him on a wild ride, up hill and down dale and through bush and briar, before abandoning him sobered and shivering in the breaking dawn light.

Leprechauns themselves were hard-working shoemakers, reported to be fabulously wealthy; a person who managed to catch one might force him to hand over a crock of gold. Leprechauns

were famously agile, however; take your eye off one for a moment, and he was gone. Two other, similar fairies shared his gnarled appearance and diminutive stature, but not his taste for hard work. The cluricauns were party-loving leprechauns, usually found drunk in rich men's wine cellars or else riding on the back of sheep, which they would leave sweating and exhausted. As for the *gancanagh* or "love-talker", he (in Yeats's words) "appears in lonely valleys, always with a pipe in his mouth, and spends his time in making love to shepherdesses and milkmaids".

The Celtic fairyland

The trooping fairies were a very different breed. They inhabited a parallel world to the human one, both enticing and dangerous. There was some uncertainty about their origins. According to myth, they were descendants of the Tuatha de Danaan, the people of the goddess Danu, who were early inhabitants of Ireland. Defeated by the human Milesians, they were forced to take refuge underground beneath fairy mounds – sometimes small hills, but more often tumuli associated with Bronze Age burial sites. The most famous was the imposing passage grave at Newgrange in County Meath.

Even so, other elements also found their way into the mythic mix. Memories of ancient gods, outlawed with the coming of Christianity, were also preserved in fairy lore. Queen Mab, ruler of a fairy host, recalled Medb, a legendary queen who represented one aspect of the Celtic mother goddess, while Morgan le Fay, a sinister figure in the Arthurian legends, could trace her descent to the ferocious female war deity known as the Morrigan. Then again, there were aspects of early

> "The party-loving cluricauns were usually found drunk in rich men's wine cellars or else riding on the back of sheep, which they would leave sweating and exhausted."

nature spirits in the fairies' pedigree, for they were closely associated with specific features of the landscape, including lakes and caves as well as mounds. Fairy rings – circles of dark green grass in pastures and meadows, sometimes circled with mushrooms – were seen as their work, marking the places where they staged their nighttime dances. Prosaically, botanists now trace the rings' origins to

93

CHANGELINGS

Some of the most disturbing stories of human–fairy interactions concerned the propensity of fairy mothers for stealing mortal babies from their cradles. In their place they would leave changelings – fairy infants that were often wizened or deformed. To avoid that fate, nervous mothers sought to protect their offspring by placing objects repellent to fairies close to the crib – Bibles or crosses, as they were pagan, or else cold steel in the form of scissors or blades. Parents who thought a switch had been made would sometimes barbarously hold a flame to the

child's skin, for it was thought that fire forced the usurpers to reveal their true identity; at such times the fairy mother might suddenly appear, offering to return the human child to save her own from pain.

If allowed to grow up in the human world, the fairy children often revealed special talents, such as second sight or the ability to make beautiful music. Human children brought up by fairies could also fare well, like Lancelot in the Arthurian legends, stolen in infancy by the Lady of the Lake.

a subterranean fungus, *Marasmius oreades*, whose presence increases the nitrogen content of the soil.

Above all, though, the Celtic fairyland contained echoes of a land of the dead. It not only lay underground and was associated with burial places but also, like the Greek Hades or the Norse Hel, was often approached across water – one example being the realm of the Lady of the Lake, a fairy queen from the Arthurian cycle.

Special rules applied to those humans who found their way into the fairy Otherworld. One such was Thomas of Erceldoune (Earlston, near Melrose in the Scottish Borders region), better known today as Thomas the Rhymer. A thirteenth-century ballad described how, while walking in the Eildon Hills one day, he saw and fell in love with a lady on a white horse bedecked with silver bells. When he kissed her, she revealed her identity as the queen of Elphame (fairyland) and took him back with her to her magic realm. He stayed there, forbidden to talk, for what seemed to him only a short time; yet when he was finally allowed to return home, he found that seven years had passed. With him he brought the gift of second sight, and he subsequently won a reputation not just as a poet but also as a seer.

The tale of Janet and Tam Lin

The Scottish borders came second only to Ireland in the wealth of its fairy lore. A second, darker tale from the same region told of Tam Lin, a handsome fairy being who haunted the plain of Carterhaugh, at the confluence of the Ettrick and

---

THE PERIS OF PERSIA

The Victorian concept of fairies as ethereal, gossamer-winged beings owed much to Persian peris, popularized in the *1,001 Nights*. Peris were spirit beings who took the form of beautiful women living in magnificent palaces and feeding only on the scent of the finest perfumes. They were sworn enemies of the *divs*, malevolent entities who constantly sought to capture them, when they would lock them in iron cages and hang them from high trees.

Ironically, the peris' origins lay in the *pairikas* of the *Avesta*, the Zoroastrian holy book; agents of the evil Ahriman, these female demons often took the form of rats. The peris, however, put their unsavoury extraction far behind them, and came in time to be seen as benevolent intermediaries charged with guiding the souls of the just to Paradise.

Yarrow rivers. The girls of the area were instructed to keep well away, at the risk of losing their maidenheads. When Janet, daughter of the local laird, neglected this warning, she encountered Tam and duly fell pregnant. On a second meeting, she learned that he had once been "an earthly knight" who had fallen under the spell of the Queen of the Fairies and now lived as one of her lieges in her kingdom under a nearby hill. He feared to stay there, though, for each year the fairies had to pay the tithe of a soul to Hell, and he sensed that his turn was coming soon.

So, at Tam's bidding, Janet vowed to rescue him and restore him to the human world. He told her to wait that Halloween at Miles Cross, where the fairy host would ride, and watch until she saw him – he would be riding a milk-white steed. If she could pull him from the horse and clutch him to her no matter what happened, she could win him from the fairies' power.

Bravely Janet did as she was told, holding on grimly even when the fairy queen used her magic to shape-shift the creature in Janet's arms into a newt, then an adder, then a bear, and finally into a lion. At last Janet was left cradling "a naked knight", whose nudity she covered with a green mantle. Then, with the fairy queen looking on in impotent rage,

she was able to bear Tam triumphantly back to the human world to be a father to her child.

There were many tales of humans taking fairy lovers, but few ended as happily. More typically, the essential incompatibility of the human and fairy worlds ultimately intervened, tragically separating the couples. In Irish legend the warrior Oisin fell in love with the fairy princess Niamh when he saw her riding on the shores of Lough Leane, near modern Killarney. They lived happily in the Otherworld and had three children, but Oisin could not overcome his longing to see his earthly home once more. At last Niamh let him go on a visit, warning him that he must remain on horseback at all times and not set foot on Irish soil. But Oisin was thoughtless, and stepped down to wash himself at a trough. At once he aged 300 years, turning from a handsome youth into a wizened old man. He spent his last years tended by St Patrick, newly arrived in Ireland, as a bard telling tales of the heroic days of his youth.

The moral, as so often, was that the human and fairy spheres could not mix. Those who dreamed of fairyland, like the man in the Yeats poem, were doomed to perpetual discontent, exiled under grey mortal skies.

95

Tree Spirits Wood nymphs and lords of the forest

Appearance
Dryads took the form of beautiful women; the Slav *leszi* usually appeared as wizened old men.

Size
Dryads were human-sized, but the *leszi* was a shape-shifter who could take any size.

Lifespan
Long-lived, but not immortal. Hamadryads died when the trees they personified were felled.

Powers
Shape-shifting. The ability to bring harm on humans who damaged trees or forest life.

Habitat
Woods and forests.

Anyone who has been in great woods at dawn or twilight, when the air is still and the leaves are barely stirring, has likely felt a sense of hidden presences watching from the surrounding shades. Various cultures have chosen to personify that awareness in the form of tree spirits, whether in the form of a Lord of the Forest or of supernatural beings sheltering in individual trees.

The classical world opted for the latter version in the female nymphs known as dryads; there were also hamadryads, linked to specific trees, who died if their tree was felled. The nearest the classical world came to a forest lord was Silvanus, the Roman god of woods, to whom herders offered sacrifices to protect the cattle that wandered within them.

Correctly, dryads were the spirits of oak trees; meliae were ash-nymphs, and there were also myrtle-nymphs, credited with having taught the culture hero Aristaeus (and through him humankind) such useful arts as cultivating olives, constructing beehives and curdling milk to make cheese.

Aristaeus played a part in another myth involving dryads. It was in fleeing his unwanted advances that Orpheus's wife Eurydice was bitten by the snake that killed her. Subsequently Artistaeus's bees all died. Distraught, the god sought help from an oracle, and was told to sacrifice four bulls and four heifers to the dryads who had been Eurydice's closest companions. He did so, and from the carcasses new swarms of bees arose – a story oddly reminiscent of the biblical account of Samson taking honey from the body of a dead lion.

Classical myth also told stories of mortal women transformed into trees.

GERMANY'S FOREST GUARDIANS

Like the Slav lands, Germany had a tradition of forest guardians in the shape of the *waldgeister*, literally "spirits of the wood". The *waldgeist* resembled the *leszi* (see page 98), but for the most part was a more benevolent presence, at least for well-disposed visitors to his domain. Even so, anyone entering a wooded area was well advised to win the spirit's goodwill by offering a gesture of respect. The notion that it is lucky to knock on wood reportedly came from the German woodsman's habit of gently tapping on the trunk of some ancient forest giant to salute the local *waldgeist* who might be watching his every move.

Phyllis, a Thracian princess, pined away waiting for her lover Acamas to return from the Trojan War and was turned by the goddess Athene into an almond tree. Dionysus changed his beloved Carya, daughter of a Spartan king, into a walnut tree following her death. Most famously of all, the mountain nymph Daphne, pursued by the lustful Apollo, appealed for help to the Earth Mother Gaia (some sources say the river god Peneus, her father) and was magicked into a laurel.

Terrors of the taiga

Such elegant fantasies were well suited to the graceful beauty of Mediterranean trees and groves, but hardly captured the spirit of the great northern forests. There Slav mythology handed down stories of the *leszi*, threatening presences that echoed the awe and fear the spruce and pine expanses of the taiga inspired.

In his own right, the *leszi* was usually visualized as a towering man. He was a shape-shifter, though, and often chose to appear to travellers as a wizened ancient, found seated by some woodland track; only his glowing eyes and the fact that his shoes faced backwards gave away his true identity. Wise wayfarers took steps to propitiate the *leszi* before venturing into a forest, perhaps by making the sign of the cross or else by leaving a small offering of bread or tobacco.

The *leszi's* delight was to misdirect strangers so that they became hopelessly lost or fell victim to wild beasts. He was a protector of the forest's animal and plant life, so woodsmen who felled trees or huntsmen who killed game always risked his wrath. Bears and wolves were his special protectors, warning him of alien presences among the thickets and guarding him from harm. The spirits could swell to enormous size when challenged, and people sometimes blamed storm damage in woods on the havoc caused by two *leszi* fighting each other. Similarly, whirlwinds were said to be stirred up by their swirling wedding dances.

The sad tale of Higo and Heitaro

Medieval Japan was also a land of thick forests, and it too had its tree spirits. The *kodama* inhabited trees and rocks,

> "Wise wayfarers took steps to propitiate the *leszi* before venturing into a forest, perhaps by making the sign of the cross or else by leaving a small offering of bread or tobacco."

THE WILD WOODWOSE

The woodwose or wodwo was the wild man of the woods of medieval legend, allied to the ubiquitous nature spirit known as the Green Man. Naked, unkempt and hairy, his image cropped up in church carvings, manuscript illuminations and armorial bearings. Similar figures also appeared in literature, notably in Geoffrey of Monmouth's *Life of Merlin*, which described how the prophet took to the woods when driven mad by his lord's defeat in the sixth-century Battle of Arthuret.

A thirteenth-century Norse chronicle contained a description of a real-life woodwose captured in a Norwegian forest: "No one could say for sure if it was a man or some other animal . . . . It had the human shape, however, in every detail, but the entire body was covered with hair as the beasts are, and down the back it had a long, coarse mane like that of a horse, which fell to both sides and trailed along the ground when the creature stooped in walking."

and were held responsible for echoes, caused when they imitated human voices. The *kino-o-bake*, in contrast, was a shape-shifter who could assume various guises, but if disturbed would disappear into the trunk or leaves of a tree.

The close sense of identification that some Japanese felt with trees came over clearly in the traditional story of the willow wife. It told of a young farmer, Heitaro, whose favourite recreation was to sit beneath the great willow tree that had long flourished in the village where he lived. For years he tended it and protected it from harm. Then, one evening as he rested under its canopy, he found himself sharing its shade with a beautiful young woman he had never seen before. The two started talking, and she told him that her name was Higo ("Willow"). Before long he fell in love with her, and they were married.

The two lived together happily for years, and Higo bore her husband a child. Then word came to the village that the Emperor Toba wished to build a great temple in Kyoto and that every community was expected to provide timber. Their contribution was to be the great willow. The wife turned pale on hearing the news. That night Heitaro was woken by a terrible scream.

"They are cutting down the willow," he heard Higo cry. "I am its spirit, and if it dies, so do I."

At that moment there was a rending crash as the great tree fell. Distraught, Heitaro turned back to his wife, only to find an empty bed. Like a Greek hamadryad, Higo was gone forever.

Unicorn Horned horses that only virgins could tame

Appearance
A white horse with the forelegs of an antelope, the beard of a goat, and a long, twisted horn protruding from its forehead.

Size
"A very small animal, like a kid", according to one medieval bestiary – but the Roman writer Aelian claimed the Indian unicorn was the size of a mature horse.

Lifespan
Unspecified – presumably similar to the dozen or so years most horses could expect to live in the wild.

Powers
Exceptional speed – no hunter could catch it. Also fierce, and brave enough to fight elephants.

Habitat
Typically woodland, although one tradition maintained that unicorns kept to deserts and the tops of mountains. The earliest Western accounts had them living in India, although the Greek traveller Herodotus believed they came from Libya.

Few creatures have developed a symbolism as dense or as contradictory as that of the unicorn. The snow-white beast with its long single horn has been seen as an image of sexual love and of chastity, of ferocity and of healing, of untamed passion and of Jesus Christ. Yet it was for long accepted as a real animal, and the belief that unicorns' horn served as an antidote to poison was so entrenched that French kings drank from vessels purportedly made of the substance until the revolution of 1789.

Most of the beliefs about unicorns can be traced back to just two or three written sources. The earliest was an account by the Greek Ctesias, who worked as a physician at the Persian court in the fourth century BCE. Writing of the wildlife of India, he described animals the size of horses or larger, with white bodies and purple heads from which a single horn about 18 inches (45cm) long protruded from the centre of the forehead. This horn was also white at the base but black in the middle and crimson at the tip. They were swift runners – so fast that no horse could overtake them. They fought fiercely, kicking with their hoofs and biting with their teeth, and no hunter could capture them. Ctesias also first spelled out the healing properties of unicorn horn: "Those who drink from these horns, made into drinking vessels, are not subject, they say, either to convulsions or the falling sickness. Indeed, they are immune even to poisons …". Later writers would expand on this belief to include the notion that unicorns could purify polluted water simply by dipping their horns in it as they drank.

Further sightings

In the wake of Ctesias and Megasthenes (see box, page 102), reports of unicorn-like beasts started cropping up from other parts. Julius Caesar, not noted for his credulity, reported the existence of "an ox, shaped like a stag, from whose forehead rises a single horn" in the forests of Germany. A later Roman writer, Aelian, specified that the horn was spiral in form. There were also other, non-classical traditions, to judge from a drawing

THE ELUSIVE MONOCEROS

After Ctesias, the major Western source for the unicorn legend was another Greek traveller, Megasthenes, who journeyed to India in about 300 BCE. His work is now lost, but fragments survive in the works of later classical authors, notably Pliny the Elder, who seemingly relied on it for information about an animal he called the monoceros. Pliny's monoceros was a fierce creature with the body of a horse, a staglike head, elephant's feet and the tail of a boar. It had a deep bellow, a single black horn 3 feet (90cm) long, and, like the unicorn, could not be hunted down.

The monoceros became confounded in subsequent literature with Ctesias's unicorn, although it now seems likely that Pliny and Megasthenes were actually passing on second-hand information about a genuine creature, the Indian rhinoceros (*Rhinoceros unicornis*). Interestingly, Indian tradition has long claimed medicinal properties for powdered rhino horn, among them the power to counteract the effect of poisons.

---

from an Egyptian satirical papyrus dated to 1200 BCE. This shows a lion and a unicorn sitting on stools playing a draughts-like boardgame called *senit*.

A virgin's lap

Another crucial part of the unicorn legend made its first appearance in the *Physiologus*, an influential collection of animal lore written between the second and fourth centuries CE. This work claimed that the beasts could be captured only in a very unusual way: "Men lead a virgin to the place where he resorts and leave her there alone. As soon as he sees the virgin, he runs to lay his head in her lap. She caresses him, and he falls asleep. The hunters then come up and capture him."

This passage was to inspire one of the most original and delightful themes of medieval art. Among other examples, the unicorn hunt provided the subject matter for a famous set of seven tapestries now in the Metropolitan Museum of Art in New York, as well as a similar set in Paris's Cluny Museum. The motif came to have multiple meanings. To post-Freudian eyes the symbolism of the fierce unicorn and its rampant horn tamed in a virgin's lap seems obvious enough, but in the Middle Ages people saw things differently. Then the virgin quickly became identified with the Virgin Mary, and the unicorn came to stand for Christ himself, born of a virgin womb and subsequently captured by persecutors who had him crucified.

Alongside this religious connotation, however, was another, chivalric interpretation of the theme that chose rather to read into the unicorn's demise the fate of the impassioned knight undone by love.

Antidote to poisons

Meanwhile the medicinal properties of unicorn horn (or "alicorn", as it came to be known) had not been forgotten. In an age when kings and princes employed tasters to test their drinks for poison, alicorn became a hugely desirable commodity, and large sums were paid for supposed horns. The Renaissance sculptor and goldsmith Benvenuto Cellini recounts in his *Autobiography* how Pope Clement VII commissioned him in 1532 to furnish a design for mounting a unicorn's horn, "the finest which had ever been seen", for which the pope had paid the huge sum of 17,000 ducats. Clement subsequently presented the horn to France's King Francis I on the occasion of the marriage of the king's son to Catherine de Medici. Many such horns still survive in museums and cathedral treasuries, and have been shown to come not from unicorns but from the narwhal, the spiral-tusked Arctic whale.

The lucrative alicorn market helped keep belief in unicorns alive beyond the Renaissance. Increasingly, however, sceptical voices made themselves heard. The reforming Council of Trent formally banned the religious use of unicorn symbolism in a decree of 1563. In the mid-seventeenth century a Danish zoologist named Ole Worm finally identified narwhals as the true source of alicorn.

Yet the old beliefs still lingered on. Sightings of unicorns continued to be reported, always from the farthermost limits of the travelled world. In 1673 a Doctor Lappe maintained that they inhabited the great woodlands of North America; by the early nineteenth century the last reports had them living in the deserts of Outer Mongolia and the mountains of Tibet. Then, finally, belief faded, and unicorns lived on in art and literature in a purely symbolic role, as an image of purity too immaculate to survive in the tainted real world.

"The symbolism of the unicorn and its rampant horn tamed in a virgin's lap seems obvious enough, but in the Middle Ages people saw things differently."

Qilin China's propitious unicorn

Appearance
A single-horned animal with the body of a deer, the hooves of a horse and the tail of an ox. The horn was alternatively described as short and fleshy or 12ft (3m) long.

Size
Stag-sized.

Lifespan
1,000 years.

Powers
Instinctively distinguished guilt from innocence. Normally entirely pacific, it could spit fire when it saw virtue persecuted by wickedness.

Habitat
Only appeared in lands governed by just rulers.

A story from the dawn of Chinese history describes how a minister of justice named Gao Yao judged the cases brought before him. He relied on the aid of a beast part horse, part goat and part deer, with a single horn in the middle of its forehead and a nature so pure it could instinctively tell right from wrong. With its horn it would gently butt the guilty party, indicating who was to blame. Taking credit for its sure judgment, Gao Yao came to be revered as another Solomon for his wisdom and is still honoured today in the vast Chinese pantheon as the god of justice.

Gao Yao's helper was a qilin, often described as the Chinese unicorn. The beast was solitary, and did not mate. Its name was made up of two ideograms representing respectively "male" and "female", so it contained within it an exact balance of the active and passive elements, yin and yang.

The qilin, then, was a model of perfection. Its nature was so gentle that it would eat no living thing, subsisting entirely on dead plant matter. So light was its tread that it could pass over grass without flattening it, and it took care never to step on any creature, however

---

TRESPASSERS WILL BE EXECUTED

Arab legend had its own stories of a unicorn-like creature, the karkadann. Unlike the qilin, though, it was a ferocious beast, willing to take on all comers intruding on its territory in the plains of Persia and northern India. Its victims included elephants, and when it killed them it would raise their dead bodies, skewered on its horn, in triumph toward the Sun until it was blinded by the melted fat running into its eyes.

The elephant story echoes tales told by the Greek traveller Megasthenes about the monoceros (see page 102), which suggests that the two animals might have been one and the same. If so, both may derive from second-hand descriptions of the Indian rhinoceros. Another intriguing possibility is that they reflect accounts of the elasmotherium, an extinct giant rhino that could conceivably have survived on the plains of southern Russia into historic times. Rhinoceros-like in its general appearance, the elasmotherium weighed up to 5 tonnes and was 20 feet (6m) long, with a single horn 7 feet (2.1m) long on its broad head.

minute. It was swift-footed and could never be caught alive. In any case, only the rashest hunters would have sought to pursue one, for to wound a qilin was a sure recipe for persistent bad luck.

A beast of such exquisite sensibility was almost too good for the world, and so qilins only appeared in exceptional times, when a great man was either ruling the nation or exerting his influence over it. Ancient chronicles claimed that one graced the garden of the legendary Yellow Emperor, Huang Di, a culture hero credited with bringing many of the benefits of civilization to China. A pair existed in the time of the Emperor Yao, Confucius's model ruler, while there were also a couple of sightings associated with the great sage himself. One supposedly was spotted at the time of his birth, while at the end of his life word came that unthinking hunters had shot another down. Confucius had no doubt what the news meant, seeing in the beast's demise a portent of his own coming death.

Stories of qilins persisted into historic times. The

Emperor Yongle sent the eunuch admiral Zheng He on a series of epic voyages of exploration into the Indian Ocean. He returned from one such trip in 1414 bearing a gift from the Sultan of Malindi in what is now Kenya: a giraffe, never before seen in China. Diplomatically, the unfamiliar animal was presented to the great Ming ruler as a qilin.

Tarasque Voracious amphibian tamed by St Martha

Appearance
"A great dragon, half beast and half fish", with a head like a lion's, a serpent's tail, and two wings on either side. Often shown with 6 sharp-clawed legs.

Size
"Greater than an ox, longer than a horse".

Lifespan
Unspecified, but one popular version of the story has it plaguing the district for 3 times 7 years.

Powers
As strong as 12 lions or bears, with teeth as sharp as swords and a taste for human flesh. Also the ability to defecate fiery ordure over those who pursued it for "the space of an acre of land".

Habitat
The River Rhône near Tarascon in France.

Jacobus de Voragine's *The Golden Legend* has many tales of saints conquering dragons. Few, though, are as celebrated as his account of the monster he called Tarasconus and its taming at the hands of the gentle St Martha.

Martha is, of course, herself a well-known figure in the New Testament. Sister of Mary and brother of Lazarus who was brought back from the dead,

she and all her family were loved by the Lord. As de Voragine tells the story, she took ship after Christ's resurrection and was carried to the mouth of the River Rhône in France. She subsequently set about the task of spreading the Christian message to the people inhabiting the lower reaches of the river.

There she found the local inhabitants living in fear of a voracious monster. The tarasque had come into the country from Galicia in Spain, where it had been born of an unholy union between the primeval sea serpent Leviathan (see pages 200–203) and the cowlike bonnacon (see pages 114–115). This fearsome creature had taken up its abode in a wood bordering the river midway between Arles and Avignon. From its lair it spread terror across the surrounding countryside and also on the river itself, for it was amphibious; if travellers on land were not safe, neither were those on boats, which it also attacked.

Promising to rid the district of the pest, Martha bravely ventured to its den in the woods. Her courage did not fail her even when she found it devouring its latest victim. Instead she cast holy water on it and showed it the cross, whereupon the monster "was overcome, and stood still as a sheep". She was then able to bind it with her girdle. Hearing the news, the people the beast had terrorized hurried to cut it down with spears and swords. Martha subsequently took up residence in the wood where the tarasque had lived, leading an ascetic life, "eschewing flesh and all fat meat, eggs, cheese and wine". After her death a church was built there in her honour, and the town of Tarascon grew up around it. Local tradition still maintains that the church is Martha's burial place.

If the tarasque is still well remembered today, it is because the town never forgot its saintly benefactor. Now as in the past, a representation of the monster is paraded through the streets of Tarascon on the last Sunday of June each year. With a head that suggests the cowardly lion of *The Wizard of Oz* and a body resembling a spiked snail's shell, the float that currently embodies it is more endearing than terrifying, scaring only the smallest of the children at whom the festivities are now aimed.

THE 'OBBY 'OSS OF PADSTOW

If the history of the tarasque of Tarascon is relatively well documented, the origins of the 'Obby 'Oss, celebrated each year at Padstow on the north coast of Cornwall, is shrouded in mystery. The name is dialect for "hobby-horse", the stick horses that served as children's playthings in pre-industrial times. Each May morning a dancer representing the 'Obby 'Oss parades through the town wearing a costume whose main feature is a horizontal hoop draped with a black cape and bearing a stylized horse's head. The 'Obby 'Oss (there have been two concurrently in recent years) makes playful lunges at any single girl passing by, and tradition has it that those caught under the cape will be pregnant within the year. The date of the festival and its mildly provocative theme suggest that it is a survival of some ancient fertility rite, perhaps connected with the ancient Celtic fire festival of Beltane, which was also celebrated on May Day. As for the 'Oss itself, that would make it the folkloric remnant of some mighty stallion of legend, in stud for evermore.

107

Yet, in bedtime stories, imaginative narrators still compete to add gruesome details to their accounts of the tarasque's ravages, multiplying the numbers of its victims and vying to outdo each other in picturing the horrid ways in which they died. Some claim the beast was so ugly that no human eye could look on it, others that its breath was so fetid that to breathe it was to die. But all agree that it was finally tamed by the lovingkindness of the white-robed, barefoot young woman, pointing an obvious moral that Christian charity can triumph over evil even in its basest and most savage forms.

Chimera Hybrid fire-breather slain by Bellerophon

Appearance
According to Homer, a lion in front, a serpent behind, and a goat in between.

Size
Unspecified, but generally depicted as lion-like.

Lifespan
Cut short in its prime by the hero Bellerophon.

Powers
Blasted fire at every breath.

Habitat
Lycia (now in southwestern Turkey), in the valley of the Xanthus River (today called the Koca).

Homer and other classical sources tell the story of Bellerophon, who spurned the advances of Queen Anteia of Tiryns. Rejected, she got her revenge by telling her husband he had tried to rape her. Unwilling to kill a guest, the king sent Bellerophon to Lycia, the realm of Anteia's father Iobates, with a sealed note asking Iobates to dispatch him. Iobates duly gave the young hero the seemingly fatal task of ridding the kingdom of the chimera. This fearsome hybrid creature was just one of the monstrous offspring of the hundred-headed Typhon and his sister Echidna, half woman and half serpent. Their incestuous union had also given birth to the Hydra and three-headed Cerberus, the hound of Hades.

By general consent the chimera combined elements of the lion, the goat and the serpent, but sources differ on how they came together. Homer indicated that the monster had a lion's foreparts and a serpent's hindquarters, with a goat's body in between. Hesiod in his *Theogony*, however, gave it three separate heads, presumably one for each constituent part. The best-known classical representation of the beast, an Etruscan bronze dating from the fourth century BCE, shows it with a lion's head and a snake for a tail, while a goat's head emerges from its back.

By all accounts, the chimera breathed fire. To kill it, Bellerophon first tamed the flying horse Pegasus, then flew over his quarry, riddling it with arrows. Once it was weakened, he thrust his spear into its mouth, having earlier tipped the lance with lead. The monster's fiery breath melted the metal, which ran down its throat, choking it and searing its innards until it died.

The chimera never made a very convincing monster. The parts were too disparate, failing to coalesce as satisfactorily as those of such other hybrids as the sphinx or the Minotaur. As a result it rather faded from view. It survives today in English in the adjective "chimerical", used to describe something wildly fantastical and improbable, an illusion that ultimately comes to nothing.

Cynocephali Dog-headed people of medieval legend

Appearance
Dog-headed humans.

Size
Human.

Lifespan
The normal mortal span.

Powers
No superhuman attributes.

Habitat
Herodotus thought they lived in Ethiopia; Marco Polo put them on the Andaman Islands in the Indian Ocean.

While recording his sea voyage from China to India in the 1290s, Marco Polo described the inhabitants of the Andaman Islands thus: "You can take it for a fact that all the men of this island have heads like dogs, and teeth and eyes like dogs; I can assure you that the whole aspect of their faces is that of big mastiffs."

Polo's account does not make it clear whether he personally visited the islands.

BALTIC DOG-PEOPLE

A different tradition of human–dog hybrids survived in the folklore of the eastern Baltic region. The *koerakoonlased* of Estonian legend had canine heads with a single eye in the middle of their foreheads. Unlike the cynocephali, however, their bodies were half human and half dog, divided down the middle, with a hand and a foot on one side, for instance, but paws on the other.

These creatures were fearsome predators who preyed on humans, feasting their children on their victims' flesh. They could only be driven away by the scent of buckthorn, a shrub whose toxic berries were used in past times as a purgative. Similar legends circulated among the Latvians and to a lesser extent the Lithuanians. In time the *koerakoonlased* became synonymous with unfamiliar, presumed savage peoples. Estonians getting their first glimpse of Cossacks at the time of the Crimean War are said to have christened them "dogheads".

Chances are that he did not, for he was in fact peopling them with a legendary dog-headed race reported in many different parts of the world at least from classical times. The Greek Ctesias, a physician based at the Persian court, credited them with horses' necks, while Herodotus claimed that they breathed fire.

Similar stories were also told in China. In 499 CE the Buddhist missionary Hui Shen visited Fusang, a country he described as lying 20,000 *li* (maybe 1,000 miles/1,500 km) across the China Sea. He too reported the existence of an island of dog-headed people, in his case somewhere off Fusang's eastern shore.

Some of the classical tales may have been inspired by Egyptian depictions of the jackal-headed god Anubis. Another theory traces the story to baboons, monkeys that have dog-like muzzles; even today the scientific name for the Yellow baboon of East Africa is *Papio cynocephalus*.

Whatever the origin of the stories, they circulated widely in medieval times. Many authorities, from Isidore of Seville to Adam of Bremen, not only confirmed

the dog people's existence but described them with varying amounts of circumstantial detail. They even found their way into Vincent of Beauvais's *Speculum Naturale* ("Mirror of the Natural World"), the most widely consulted encyclopedia known to thirteenth-century Europe. It reported that cynocephali behaved like humans when peaceful, but if aroused reverted to savagery.

The most curious story of all was that of St Christopher, still familiar as the patron saint of travellers. Western tradition described him as a giant who ferried voyagers on his shoulders over a river until one day he met the Christ child and was converted. The story told in the Eastern Orthodox Church was very different. It maintained that in Roman times legionaries fighting in the Libyan Desert captured a dog-headed giant. The monster was subsequently persuaded to change sides and was assigned to an auxiliary unit, the Marmaritae. In his new allegiance he was baptised a Christian and began to preach the faith, eventually undergoing martyrdom in the persecutions of the Emperor Decius. Images of the saint with an unmistakably canine head survive to this day as curious survivals of an ancient and widespread tradition.

Baba Yaga Hideous hag who ate small children

Appearance
Hideous hag who ate small children.

Size
Usually described as tall and gaunt.

Lifespan
Prematurely old – in some legends she was said to age a year each time that someone asked her a question.

Powers
Flew through the air in a mortar, using a pestle for a paddle. Could raise storms. Said to have teeth of iron to rend her victims' flesh.

Habitat
The forests of old Russia, where she lived in a log cabin raised on chickens' legs.

Anyone familiar with the Grimm Brothers' story of Hansel and Gretel will recognize favourite motifs in the Slav accounts of Baba Yaga. Innocent wayfarers find their way to a glade in a deep pine forest, where they see a strange dwelling. They notice with horror that the pickets of the fence surrounding it consist of human bones, topped with skulls. As for the hut itself, Russian folklore adds a surrealistic note: it stands – and sometimes moves – on chicken legs, clearly indicating the supernatural powers of the awful creature who lives within.

In Russian, "baba" is an affectionate term for "grandmother", but Baba Yaga was no one's idea of a benevolent old lady. She was a hideous crone with something of the ogress about her, who, like the witch in the Hansel story, had a penchant for eating her victims. There are suggestions in the tales that she was once more than just a witch, and that the bogeywoman of folklore actually sprang from ancestral memories of some ancient Slav goddess – one with elemental powers who guarded

the threshold between this world and the next. Some stories associated her with horsemen representing Day, Night and the Sun; others had her travelling in company with Death, who gave her souls to eat.

Yet Baba Yaga lived on in the folk memory less for such associations than for the sheer narrative power of the stories told about her. Generations of children shivered at their grim details, all distorted from familiar everyday life: her iron teeth, sharp as knives for rending flesh; the cavernous cooking pots in which she boiled her victims. Then there were her magical powers of transport: some said she flew through the air in an iron kettle stirring up storms, others that she rode in a gigantic mortar, propelling herself with a pestle and sweeping away her slipstream with a broom of silver birch.

Unexpected benevolence

Baba Yaga was not always as fearsome as she seemed. Many tales recounted ways in which clever heroes and heroines outwitted her, sometimes even winning her goodwill by their tact and hard work.

Such was the case with Vasilissa the Beautiful, heroine of one of the most celebrated of all Russian fairy stories. Mistreated by a cruel stepmother, Vasilissa was sent into the forest to fetch light from Baba Yaga. With the aid of a magic doll that her real mother had given to her on her death bed, the girl found her way to the chicken-legged hut, but then was too scared to enter. Discovering her there that evening when she flew home in her mortar, Baba Yaga invited the terrified Vasilissa inside.

There Vasilissa was presented with a series of seemingly impossible domestic tasks that she in fact managed to perform with the doll's aid. Won over, the old witch eventually sent the girl home with the light she had come to request – actually a skull whose eye-sockets cast out a fiery glow so powerful that at first glimpse it burned up the wicked stepmother and her ugly daughters besides. As for Vasilissa, she subsequently found her way to St Petersburg, where her diligence and beauty attracted the attention of the czar himself, who married her. And so she lived happily ever after, a testament to the power of Baba Yaga's savage goodwill.

113

"Some said she flew through the air in an iron kettle stirring up storms, others that she rode in a gigantic mortar, propelling herself with a pestle and sweeping away her slipstream with a broom of silver birch."

Catoblepas & Bonnacon · Bizarre bovines

CATOBLEPAS

Appearance
Body protected with large scales, head covered in shaggy hair and held close to the ground.

Size
Medium-sized. Aelian made it as big as a domestic bull, other sources the size of a half-grown calf.

Lifespan
Unspecified.

Powers
Anyone who saw its eyes died instantly.

Habitat
Ethiopia, near the headwaters of the River Nile.

With limited opportunities for travel, the classical naturalists had to rely on second- or third-hand sources for information about the creatures inhabiting the further reaches of the known world. Inevitably, some of the stories that reached them got distorted along the way. Some such garbling went into the creation of the catoblepas and bonnacon, animals with recognizable traits that nonetheless have no real equivalents in the natural world.

Both creatures found their way into the exhaustive *Natural History* of Rome's Pliny the Elder, writing in the first century CE. He claimed that the catoblepas lived near the Nile's source in Ethiopia, describing it as "in most respects of moderate size and inactive in its limbs, but with a very heavy head that it carries with difficulty". He added that it kept its head close to the ground, which was just as well given that even a fleeting glance from its eyes was deadly for humans.

Writing 150 years after Pliny, Aelian added further details. He described the animal as being "about the size of a bull, but with a grimmer aspect, for its eyebrows are high and shaggy and the eyes beneath are not large like those of oxen but narrow and bloodshot". He also claimed that it had a mane on the crown of its head that fell over its forehead.

Aelian added a second reason for approaching the beast with care, stating that it fed on poisonous roots that made its breath noxious. If alarmed, "it emits from its throat pungent and foul-smelling breath, so that the whole air around is infected, and any animals that approach and inhale it are grievously affected, lose their voice, and are seized with fatal convulsions". Consequently other animals fled from it, and it lived a solitary life.

This description apparently caught the imagination of the great French novelist Gustave Flaubert, for he included the catoblepas among the nightmare beings afflicting the desert-father hero of his novella *The Temptation of St Anthony*. Flaubert's catoblepas addresses the saint in mournful tones, telling him that it is aware of little but the warm mud under its belly and revealing that once, in a fit of absent-mindedness, it ate its own foreleg unawares.

Baron Cuvier, the great French naturalist of the Age of Reason, suggested that accounts of the catoblepas were probably based on distorted descriptions of the gnu, with the basilisk's stare (and possibly also the pangolin's scales) thrown in for good measure. Some similar misapprehensions must also have shaped classical notions of the bonnacon, which according to Pliny was found in Paeonia – at the time a little-known area north of Macedon on the outer fringes of the Greek world.

A formidable defence

The beast Pliny described was bovine in its general appearance but had a mane like that of a horse. Its horns curved back, and so were useless for fighting. Instead, it relied, skunk-like, on excretion for its defence. If attacked, it would take to flight, leaving behind a devastating trail of fiery dung. This napalm-like emission could set fire to trees and shrubs and would scorch the hair off hunting dogs unlucky enough to be touched by it.

The bonnacon was something of a favourite of the medieval bestiarists, and more than a dozen manuscripts contain references to it. The illustrations accompanying the texts followed Pliny's description in suggesting some large ruminant. One possible candidate would be the European bison, which became extinct in the wild in 1919, although it has now been reintroduced in Poland's Bialowieza Forest and elsewhere. The auroch, which roamed parts of eastern Europe as late as the seventeenth century, has also been mentioned, but this large ox, now completely vanished, is generally held to have had straight and lethal horns. And while most large herbivores excrete warm dung, no physiological feature of either animal could in any way explain the combustible nature of the bonnacon's faeces – a dramatic but inexplicable detail that can only be put down to the inventive capacity of the human imagination.

BONNACON
Appearance
The body of a horse and the head of a bull with curved horns. (See illustration, above.)

Size
Bull-sized.

Lifespan
Unspecified.

Powers
Defended itself by emitting fiery dung that could cover an area as much as three *stadia* (600yds or 550m) in extent.

Habitat
According to Pliny the Elder, Paeonia – now the region north of the Republic of Macedonia in the eastern Balkans.

Grendel Cannibalistic swamp-demon killed by Beowulf

Appearance
Monstrous swamp creature with talons for hands.

Size
Large, but not too big for Beowulf to take on in single combat.

Lifespan
Cut short by the hero Beowulf.

Powers
Immense strength and cannibalistic appetites. Also some amphibious attributes.

Habitat
A mere near the mead-hall of the Danish king Hrothgar, set among "wolf-haunted hills, windswept crags, and perilous fen-tracks".

The great hall flamed bright with torches in the early-morning hours, but in the darkness outside something was moving. The creature lurching toward the glowing building from the mist-shrouded mere where it lived had a terrible purposefulness in its stride. For blood was on its mind – the blood of Danish warriors sleeping off the effects of a midwinter night's carousing in the royal house of Heorot.

Grendel was a creature of the darkness, and he hated the light and all who dwelled within it. Born of the brood of Cain, he was cursed to inhabit a netherworld, neither human nor animal, in the lake-bed dwelling he shared with his equally monstrous mother. There the two brooded in bitter solitude, and the more they fretted over their fate the more they longed for revenge. Grendel satisfied the craving by nocturnal forays to human haunts, where he wreaked bloody havoc, rending and tearing the recumbent forms of the feasters as they slept.

Beowulf and the "corpse-demon"

Grendel was, of course, the monstrous being confronted by the hero Beowulf in the Anglo-Saxon poem of that name. One of the earliest of world literature's Gothic monsters, he was also among the most fearsome, a creature of pure evil that the poem's Christian author sought by every descriptive kenning – "hell-serf", "corpse-demon", "dark-prowler" – to paint as one of the damned. Cannibalistic in his appetites, he must have stirred terror in spellbound listeners thrilling to his exploits by rush lamp or candlelight, much as the creatures that inhabit horror films do for current generations shivering in the cinema's warmer dark.

"No sword could penetrate his scaly hide, so the final battle was a trial of strength that ended when the hero wrenched Grendel's entire arm from its socket."

Scholars have struggled to find antecedents for Grendel in earlier Germanic or Norse legend. The monster's giant size seems to link him with the trolls (see pages 182–183), a connection also suggested by his nocturnal habits, for trolls hated the light of day. Some of his fighting qualities may have come from the berserkers, Viking warriors who worked themselves into a blind fury before going into battle.

Driven by spite

A more likely influence, however, may have been stories of draugs (see page 66), reanimated corpses that rose from the grave and were able to change their size and shape at will. Draugs famously envied the joys of the living, just as Grendel was maddened by the sounds of feasting in Heorot each night, reminding him of pleasures he could never share.

Icelandic sagas would later describe titanic struggles in which human adversaries overcame draugs in hand-to-hand combat. Grendel fell victim in similar fashion to Beowulf, who waited among the sleepers in the hall to seize, in an iron grip, the talon that served the creature for a hand. No sword could penetrate his scaly hide, so the final battle was a trial of strength that ended when the hero

wrenched Grendel's entire arm from its socket. With blood pouring from the gaping wound, the fiend limped back to the mere to die – leaving his grieving mother fresh cause to seek vengeance on the hated human race.

Kitsune Fox spirits of Japanese legend

Appearance
Foxes in human form, usually appearing as beautiful maidens or old men.

Size
Seemingly normal humans.

Lifespan
Upward of 1,000 years. Older foxes grew additional tails, up to a maximum of nine.

Powers
Innumerable. Besides shape-shifting they could include the ability to read people's minds, to see into the future, to fly, to possess individuals, and to create illusions that perfectly mimic reality.

Habitat
Principally Japan, although similar traditions exist in China and Korea.

Japanese legend relates that the twelfth-century Japanese emperor Toba once gave a feast in his summer palace to which all the most talented and beautiful of his courtiers were invited. As the company dined to the accompaniment of music, darkness suddenly filled the hall where they had gathered. Rushing outside, the guests found that there too all was murk and gloom, while a great wind had risen from nowhere to howl savagely through the palace halls. Desperately the guests called for a light, only to notice that an unearthly glow was emanating from a court beauty nicknamed the Jewel Maiden, known to all as the ruler's favourite mistress.

Soon after this ominous event, the emperor fell sick, and before long he was at death's door. A Shinto priest skilled in magic was summoned to examine him, and he quickly diagnosed the problem. The Jewel Maiden, he said, was not what she seemed to be. Instead, she was a kitsune – a fox in female form. Realizing her secret was out, the courtesan switched back to

animal shape and fled the court for the desolate moorlands north of Edo. There she haunted the wilderness for many years until finally redeemed by a Buddhist monk who won her from evil ways and brought her the hope of enlightenment.

Japanese myth credited foxes with great supernatural powers, from shape-shifting and second sight to the ability to breathe fire at will. The animals were believed to be incredibly long-lived, sprouting extra tails as they grew older. The oldest foxes had as many as nine tails, and possessed knowledge of all that happened in the world.

Experts in seduction

Yet even young foxes could take human form. Vixens often assumed the guise of beautiful girls to seduce men, just as the Jewel Maiden had won the affection of Emperor Toba. Male fox spirits might similarly target human women, although in their case they chose to control them spiritually, entering their bodies either through the breasts or under their fingernails. Women possessed by fox spirits were said to be suffering from *kitsune-tsuki*, a violent form of mental illness. Sufferers might foam at the mouth, yelp like beasts, speak in unnatural voices or even foreign languages, and eat food only considered suitable for foxes. *Kitsune-tsuki* continued to be offered as a diagnosis for psychosis in women into the early years of the twentieth century.

Yet by no means all foxes were evil in their intentions. There were tales of tragic love affairs with fox-women, whose long and happy relationships with human partners were brutally cut short when their true identity was eventually exposed. Sometimes they were given away by dogs, which had an uncanny ability to sniff out the vixens' vulpine nature. Mirrors and water were also dangerous, for in their reflections the shape-shifters appeared in their original fox form, not as humans. In some stories younger werefoxes were given away by their tails, although more experienced beasts apparently learned ways of magically concealing their brushes.

Messengers of Inari

Confusingly enough, foxes also played another, wholly propitious role in Japanese legend as messengers of Inari,

the much-loved rice god. Traditional iconography pictured the deity as a plump old man sitting on a sack flanked by twin foxes, but in later times he became so confused with his assistants that he himself was sometimes shown fox-faced. In this guise foxes were bringers of good fortune that could ward off evil, sometimes even serving as guardian spirits.

119

Mandrake A plant to be harvested at your peril

Appearance
Short-stemmed, long-leaved plant whose roots have an eerily humanoid appearance.

Size
Roots are said to grow to as long as 4ft (1.2m).

Lifespan
The roots are generally extracted after 2 or 3 years.

Powers
All parts of the plant are toxic, inducing drowsiness and anaesthesia. Traditionally, the root was said to emit a scream when pulled from the ground that could drive people mad or even kill them.

Habitat
Native to southern Europe.

The world of legend has many monstrous creatures, but the mandrake is a rare example of a sinister vegetable. Scientifically the name is applied to species of the genus *Mandragora*, particularly *Mandragora officinarum*, a short-stemmed plant native to southeastern Europe. (In the USA the name American mandrake is sometimes given to the mayapple, an entirely different plant.)

Mandrake concoctions have been used from ancient times as sleeping draughts and anaesthetics. Supposedly, a Carthaginian force once defeated their Roman foes by abandoning a town and leaving behind large quantities of wine laced with mandrake. Once the victors had had time to toast their "triumph", the Carthaginians returned and killed them while they slept.

Yet most of the superstition that surrounds the plant relates to its roots. Often forked at the bottom end, these can have a humanoid appearance – a resemblance that sorcerers through the ages have enhanced by pinching the top of growing plants to form a bulbous protuberance resembling a head. Unmanipulated, they can also fancifully be taken to look like the male organ, which helped spread the idea that the plant aided fertility in women. The Italian Renaissance writer Niccolò Macchiavelli, best known for his political theories, makes this belief the mainspring of the plot of his comedy of marital infidelity, *Mandragora*.

Evidence for the ancient nature of these beliefs comes from a curious passage in the Old Testament Book of Genesis. This tells how the patriarch Jacob married two sisters, Rachel and Leah. While Leah bore him three sons, Rachel remained barren. One day Leah's eldest son Reuben brought them some mandrakes, and the two women

"Legend had it that the roots had to be picked before dawn on a Friday morning, then washed and steeped in a concoction of honey, milk and blood until they stirred into life."

proceeded to argue as to who should have them. Eventually Leah conceded them to the barren Rachel, but only in return for her agreement that she might sleep with Jacob that night – and as a result Leah duly bore him another son.

Harvesting the roots was a dangerous business, for when they were pulled from the earth they were said to utter an unearthly scream that could drive men mad. The Jewish author Josephus accordingly suggested using a dog, tied to the stem, to extract the plant. In trying to follow its master, he claimed, it would pull up the root, dying in the process. The owner could then return and take away the plant for his own use.

Other, even darker beliefs circulated about the plants. They were said to grow below gallows, born of the semen hanged men ejaculated in their death throes. From such stories the notion developed that mandrake roots could take human form as mandragoras, homunculi that sorcerers employed to tell the future. Legend had it that the roots had to be picked before dawn on a Friday morning, then washed and steeped in a concoction of honey, milk and blood until they stirred into life.

J.K. Rowling has fun with the supposedly humanoid characteristics of mandrake plants in *Harry Potter and the*

Chamber of Secrets, in which a mandrake concoction is used to bring people petrified by the basilisk's stare (see page 24) back to life. Cultivated in the Hogwarts nursery, the plants go through a recognizably human development cycle. During their adolescence they start throwing loud parties, and Professor Sprout, the school's Herbology teacher, comments: "The moment they start trying to move into each other's pots, we'll know they're fully mature."

Centaur Hybrid horse–men with a taste for riot

Appearance
Hybrid beings with the head, arms and torso of men and the bodies of horses.

Size
Horse-sized.

Lifespan
Unspecified. The Roman poet Lucretius claimed they could not exist because the horse part would die before the human had reached full maturity.

Powers
Strength and endurance. The ability to fire arrows at full gallop.

Habitat
Classical Greece, at first on Mt. Pelion in Thessaly, but latterly on the Peloponnese peninsula.

Rowdy, drunken and lustful, centaurs, like satyrs, represented the beast in man. There were conflicting accounts of their origins. Some people said they were born of the union of Ixion and a cloud shaped by Zeus to resemble his wife Hera when Ixion sought to violate her. Others took the alternative view that this cloud nymph, later known as Nephele, in fact bore a child called Centaurus, and that it was this outcast son who sired the centaurs through illicit couplings with mares from the coast of Thessaly.

So said the myths. More recently, scholars have taken the view that stories of centaurs might actually have risen from a simple misunderstanding. The theory is that when the Greeks of Homer's day, who themselves did not ride, first saw Scythian horsemen on the Thessalian plain, they mistook horse and rider for a single being. To show that the idea is not as implausible as it might initially seem, some authorities have quoted reports from Mexico at the time of the Spanish conquest, when horse-riding was similarly unknown.

Conquistadors then claimed that when Mexican warriors first saw a Spanish knight fall from his horse in battle, they turned tail and fled, having previously assumed the two were physically joined.

Agents of lustful havoc

Whatever their origins, centaurs became symbols of wild, untameable lust. Most of the stories about them involved the attempted abduction of human women. During the hunt for the Caledonian Boar, two centaurs named Hylaeus and Rhaecus tried to rape the huntress Atalanta, who promptly shot them dead. Another, Eurytion, sought to steal Hercules' intended bride Deianeira and was similarly dispatched. In that case, though, the beasts had their revenge, for it was the envenomed blood of another centaur, Nessus, that finally did for Hercules when Deianeira herself unwittingly spread it on a shirt he was to wear.

The centaurs' most famous exploit, though, was the ruckus caused when they were invited to the wedding of their Thessalian neighbour, King Pirithous. Befuddled by wine, for which

> "The theory is that when the Greeks of Homer's day, who themselves did not ride, first saw the Scythian horsemen, they mistook horse and rider for a single being."

with arms and head. Earlier, in the archaic period, they had been shown less happily as men with human legs, with the bodies and hindquarters of horses tacked clumsily on behind.

An honourable exception

If most centaurs resembled the primitive yahoos of *Gulliver's Travels* more than the rational houyhnhnms, there was at least one notable exception. This was Chiron, a centaur of exceptional sagacity who served as tutor to many of the great classical heroes, among them Jason, Peleus and Theseus. It was Chiron who instructed Asclepius, god of healing, in the medicinal arts and showed the infant Achilles how to hunt and ride.

Caring and gentle, Chiron's nature was so different from that of his fellows that he was given a separate mythical lineage all of his own. He was said to have been the child of Cronos, the father of the gods, through an adulterous union with the wood nymph Philyra. To deceive his wife Rhea, Cronos took the form of a stallion, and Chiron was duly born half-horse.

Chiron lived a long and useful life, making up by his wisdom for the ravages wrought by his less sage kinsmen. When his end finally came, it was ironically brought about by Hercules,

they had no head, the creatures sought to run off with all the most attractive female guests, among them the bride Hippodamia herself. The other guests, including the hero Theseus, sprang to their host's defence, eventually driving off the miscreants and saving the womenfolk. The centaurs were subsequently forced to abandon their original home on Mount Pelion, adjoining Pirithous's kingdom, and instead migrated south to the Peloponnese.

The Centauromachy ("Struggle with the Centaurs"), as the fight became known, was a favourite theme of Greek art, featuring on the Parthenon frieze in Athens as well as on the west façade of the Temple of Zeus at Olympia. By the classical period when those masterpieces were constructed, centaurs were portrayed gracefully as horses whose necks sprouted human torsos, complete

TRICKS OF THE TIKBALANG

Other cultures besides classical Greece and Rome had horse–human hybrids of their own. Indian myth spoke of the kimpurushas and kinnaras, servants and followers of Kubera, the king of the dwarf-like Yakshas who guarded the Earth's treasures. Kimpurushas bore men's heads (but not torsos) on equine bodies; kinnaras had men's bodies with horses' heads.

The tikbalang similarly reversed the centaur model, having the head and foreparts of a black or brown horse on a man's lower body. It was a nature spirit haunting the mountain forests of the Philippines which sought to protect the natural environment from unwanted human visitors. Like the *leszi* of Slav myth (see page 98), its delight was to lead travellers astray in the woods, often sending them on lengthy detours that ended up bringing them back where they had begun. To do so it might shift shape into human form, often taking on the appearance of some acquaintance of its victims to increase its credibility. To avoid its attentions, wayfarers were advised to wear their shirts inside out and to go quietly through the woods, first taking the precaution of audibly asking the tikbalang's permission to make the journey — an important mark of respect that usually was enough to pacify the creature.

a longtime friend. On the fourth of his ten labours, to capture the Erymanthian boar, the hero found his way to Pholoe in the Peloponnese. There he was entertained by a centaur called Pholus who, at Hercules' insistence, opened a jar of strong wine given to him many years before by the god Dionysus.

The scent of the alcohol was enough to attract a herd of other centaurs, who made a rush on Pholus's cave. When Hercules drove them off, they sought refuge with Chiron, their ruler, who lived nearby. Pursuing them, the hero fired a poisoned arrow that happened to strike his old comrade. Appalled at the accident, Hercules sought to undo the damage in any way he could, but even Chiron's own great skill in healing could not mend the wound.

Chiron now found himself in agony but, as a demi-god, he could not die. Faced with the prospect of an eternity of suffering, he appealed to Zeus, who arranged a deal; the centaur voluntarily surrendered his immortality, which went to the fire-giver Prometheus instead. To preserve Chiron's memory, Zeus turned him into a constellation of the night sky, usually identified as Sagittarius the Archer. It was a fitting memorial for a sapient counsellor who brought honour and dignity to an otherwise disreputable breed.

Questing Beast Arthurian emblem of sinfulness

Appearance
Hybrid monster with a serpent's head, the body of a leopard, a lion's hindquarters, and the feet of a hart.

Size
Large, but generally in keeping with its constituent parts.

Lifespan
Lengthy but not immortal; it was eventually killed by Sir Palamedes.

Powers
Elusiveness – for many years it evaded pursuit.

Habitat
Arthurian Britain.

The medieval love of symbolism produced many memorable images, both good, like the Holy Grail and the Paradise Garden, and grim, like the Dance of Death. So, when the authors of the Arthurian romances sought to encapsulate the depravity that finally brought King Arthur's court to ruin, they looked to invent a creature that would personify its downfall. What they devised was the Questing Beast.

Sir Thomas Malory's *Morte d'Arthur* describes King Arthur's first encounter with the beast. As the king sat resting by a forest spring, "he thought he heard a noise of hounds, to the sum of thirty. And with that the king saw coming toward him the strangest beast that ever he saw or heard of; so the beast went to the well and drank, and the noise was in the beast's belly like unto the questing of thirty couple hounds".

The beast's appearance was quite as strange as the baying noises emerging from its belly. As described in Malory's French sources, it had a snake's head on the body of a leopard, with a lion's haunches and stag's feet. Hot on its heels, but too late to catch it, came a knight, Sir Pellenore, whose fate was endlessly to hunt the creature. When Arthur offered to take his place, Pellenore rebuffed the suggestion, insisting that it was his own inescapable destiny to pursue it.

The story of the beast's origins, as later explained by Merlin, were even odder than its physical attributes. It was born, the magician claimed, of a princess who had lusted after her own brother. Finding her unnatural desires unreciprocated, she listened eagerly to the promises of a demon who came to tempt her, undertaking to secure her sibling's affections if she would only sleep with him, the demon, first. The princess obliged but,

> "The prince prophesied that his sister would be punished by giving birth to a monster whose every movement would recall the baying of the dogs that killed him."

devils being what they are, her partner failed to deliver his part of the bargain. Instead he inveigled her into approaching her father with a false accusation of rape, directed at her brother. Appalled, the king condemned the young man to a terrible death, torn apart by a pack of hungry hounds. Before he died, the prince prophesied that his sister would be punished for her act by giving birth to a monster whose every movement would recall the baying of the dogs that killed him.

This unedifying tale had particular resonance in the story because of the timing of Arthur's sighting of the beast. Shortly before the encounter he had slept with a visitor to his court, Morgause, the wife of King Lot of Orkney. And, unbeknown to Arthur at the time, the queen was in fact his half-sister, born to his own mother Igraine. So Arthur had unwittingly committed incest as well as adultery, and from the act would be born Mordred, the knight whose treachery would ultimately destroy his kingdom.

The symbolism was clear enough. The Questing Beast was an image of Arthur's

lust, which had led him into terrible sin. Yet the stories still contrived to give this strand of the narrative some sort of a satisfactory ending. Although Sir Pellenore himself never succeeded in killing the creature, the Saracen knight Sir Palamedes took up the quest after Pellenore's death. At first he too seemed condemned to a Sisyphean task – but then he converted to Christianity.

Baptised, he at last managed to corner the beast, driving it into a lake where he despatched it. Even if Arthur could not escape the consequences of his misdeeds, the message proclaimed, then at least the beast itself might at Christian hands get what it merited.

127

⊙ ⊕ ⊖

Mythic Boars Tusked marauders targeted by heroes

Appearance
Generally huge and equipped with fearsome tusks (actually enlarged canine teeth).

Size
Real-life wild boars can measure up to 6ft (1.8m) long and weigh 4 hundredweight (200kg); their mythic counterparts were usually bigger.

Lifespan
In real life, up to 20 years; in myth, often determined by the heroes who hunted them.

Powers
Great speed, power and agility, sometimes accompanied by a taste for human flesh.

Habitat
Worldwide in lands where wild pigs are found. Their current distribution ranges across Eurasia from France to China and Japan, and also includes the jungles of equatorial Africa.

In past times huntsmen armed with spears and bows feared few things more than a confrontation with an angry boar. Standing up to 4 feet (1.2m) high at their heavily muscled shoulders, the animals were known for their courage and aggression. When cornered, they would often opt to charge, and their sharp tusks could do terrible damage to anyone unlucky enough to fall before them.

Unsurprisingly, then, they found their way into myths. In the Hawaiian islands, a gigantic primeval boar named Kamapua'a was credited with pushing up the island chain with his snout at the start of creation. In India, Vishnu's third avatar was as the boar Varaha (see illustration, opposite), who rescued the Earth from the ocean bottom where an evil demon had hurled it. In Persia, Verethragna, the god of victory, took the shape of a boar to defend the sun god Mithra, and in that form no force of evil could stand against him.

Boars also had a place in the Norse stories. Dwarf craftsmen fashioned the golden boar Gullinbursti for Freyr, god of fertility, to draw his chariot by day

and night, when it lit up the darkness with its glow. In Valhalla the souls of dead warriors fed on the flesh of another magical boar, Saehrimnir, that miraculously came back to life each morning so it could be hunted and eaten once again.

Above all, though, boars played a part in hero legends, sometimes as agents of destruction. When, in Greek myth, Adonis unwittingly roused the jealousy of Ares by winning Aphrodite's love, the god of war took a wild boar's form to gore him to death. The Celtic hero Diarmuid met a similar end (see box, opposite).

The thrill of the chase

More often, though, the boar came off worst in these encounters. Different cultures had tales of heroic quests with the beasts as the quarry. Welsh legend told of the hunting of Twrch Trwyth, a giant boar and its young that were pursued across Ireland and Wales into Cornwall by a posse of heroes, King Arthur among them. In Greek legend Hercules' third labour was to capture the Erymanthaean Boar, sacred to Artemis, and bring it to Mycenae alive; he did so by driving the

129

beast into a snowdrift high on Mount Erymanthus, then tangling it in a net and carrying it back slung over his shoulder. Theseus had a similar encounter with an enormous sow that had been laying waste to the region around Crommyon on the Isthmus of Corinth. And a whole host of warriors came together to chase the Calydonian Boar, sent by the goddess Artemis to ravage the lands of the king of Calydon, who had been neglecting her worship. Eventually the creature was brought down by Atalanta, one of ancient Greece's few female warrior-heroes. The coup de grâce was delivered by the ruler's son, Meleager.

THE DEATH OF DIARMUID

The Celtic warrior Diarmuid fell to a boar in Ireland's Finn mac Cumhail cycle of legends. Blessed (or cursed) with a "love-spot" that made him irresistible to women, he won the affections of Grainne, beloved of the ageing Finn, leader of the warrior band known as the Fianna. The couple eloped, and Finn pursued them for sixteen years, while Ireland fell into near-anarchy around them. Eventually Finn tracked them down to Newgrange on the River Boyne, and offered a truce, inviting Diarmuid to accompany him on a boar hunt. It was a trap. The boar was a magical beast, cursed to kill the young warrior. Too late Diarmuid realized he had been tricked. Resigned to his fate, he confronted the deadly animal, which disembowelled him even as he struck it down with his spear.

Diarmuid is believed to have founded the Clan Campbell, one of the most powerful families of Highland Scotland. The clan's crest features a boar's head – a tribute, some say, to its heroic forefather.

Sphinx Human–lion hybrids with a deadly secret

Appearance
In Egypt, a lion with a man's head; in Greece, a winged lion with a woman's head and breasts.

Size
In Egypt, monumental. The Greek sphinx was usually portrayed as smaller – about human size.

Lifespan
The Greek sphinx killed herself when the secret of her riddle was divulged.

Powers
Leonine strength and power. The Greek sphinx sometimes ate her human victims.

Habitat
First recorded in ancient Egypt. The Greek sphinx was born (of Echidna, the mother of monsters) in Ethiopia, but was sent to haunt the region around Thebes.

Although all had lion's bodies, sphinxes came in two very different forms. In Egypt, they were guardian creatures, protecting temples and tombs. The sphinx of Greek myth, however, was a solitary female monster haunting the roads around Thebes. In later times the two became confused, creating Greco-Egyptian hybrids that contained features drawn from both models.

The best known of all was the Sphinx of Giza. Carved more than 4,500 years ago and standing 240 feet (73m) long and 65 feet (20m) high, it is still one of the largest single-stone statues in the world. It took the form of a recumbent lion with a pharaoh's head – probably that of Khafra, who ruled in the twenty-sixth century BCE. The figure, which stands guard over the Great Pyramid of Khufu (Cheops), owes its name to the Greeks, who called it after their own lion-bodied monster, even though its construction predated the classical era in Greece by more than two millennia.

In addition to the Giza man-sphinx, Egyptian sculptors also carved similar creatures with the heads of rams. Ninety

such figures once lined the entrance to
the Temple of Ammon at Karnak, rams
being sacred to the god.

Whereas the Egyptian sphinxes
symbolized majesty and power, their
Greek counterpart was solitary and
malignant. She was sent by the gods
from her original homeland in Ethiopia
to the region around Thebes. There she
waylaid travellers, forcing them on pain
of death to answer a riddle. As recounted
in Sophocles' *Oedipus Tyrannus*, the
question was: "What goes on four legs
in the morning, on two at noon, and
in the evening on three?" The hero
Oedipus eventually provided the

correct response, which is humankind,
which crawls on all fours in infancy,
walks erect through adulthood, and in
old age totters with the aid of a stick.
Appalled to hear her secret divulged, the
beast hurled herself down from the rock
on which she perched to meet her death
on the boulders below.

131

⊙ ⊕ ⊖

Blemmyes & Sciapods Exotic far-off peoples

132

Appearance
Headless, blemmyes had their facial features on their chests; sciapods had a single, central leg on which they hopped.

Size
Human.

Lifespan
Similar to those of other surrounding peoples.

Powers
No special powers other than those developed to cope with their physical oddities; sciapods, for instance, could hop fast and powerfully.

Habitat
According to Pliny, the blemmyes inhabited the western Sahara Desert; sciapods were thought to live in India.

People have always hung eagerly on the tales regaled by travellers to distant lands. Sometimes, though, the stories became distorted in the telling and retelling. The Greek explorer Ctesias, for instance, almost certainly visited Britain in the fourth century BCE and then sailed on to the northern land that he called Thule. Yet later reports based on his lost work, claiming that the atmosphere there had the consistency of a jellyfish, making it impossible to walk or sail, obviously misinterpreted his account of what was most likely a freezing fog. In other words, a description of exceptional conditions was mistaken for the norm, and

the intended meaning of the original words was lost.

Similar misunderstandings found their way into reports of distant peoples, to judge from the stories that found their way into the works of the classical geographers. Pliny the Elder passed on unsourced information about a variety of African races, among them "the half-animal Goat-Pans, the Blemmyes, the Gamphasantes, Satyrs and Strapfeet". Of these the blemmyes were perhaps the most striking, having no heads (see illustration, opposite); instead, Pliny claimed, "their mouths and eyes are attached to their chests". The Roman writer seems to have drawn his information primarily from the earlier Greek traveller Herodotus, who had reported a race of headless men with their eyes in their chests in the mountains of Ethiopia. The name of *Blemmyae* that Pliny attached to them was that of a genuine tribe of Nubian nomads known from late Roman sources.

Whatever their origins, the blemmyes caught the popular imagination. They made frequent appearances in medieval

"Othello speaks of his experiences fighting among 'the cannibals that each other eat, the Anthropophagi, and men whose heads grow beneath their shoulders'."

bestiaries, and even found their way into Shakespeare's plays, where Othello speaks of his experiences fighting among "the cannibals that each other eat, the Anthropophagi, and men whose heads grow beneath their shoulders". Some authorities have seen in the stories misunderstood accounts of people adopting a hunched gait for tribal dances.

Pliny was also the major source for the sciapods. In his description of the wonders of India, he wrote of them under the name of *Monocoli*. Quoting the fourth-century BCE Greek writer Ctesias, he claimed they had only one leg and hopped with great speed. He added: "These people are also called the Umbrella-footed, because in hot weather they lie stretched out on their backs using their feet to protect them from the sun's glare" (see illustration, page 134). In passing, he added that they lived close to the Troglodytes or Cave-dwellers, "and farther to the east are some people without necks and with eyes in their shoulders" – apparently a second

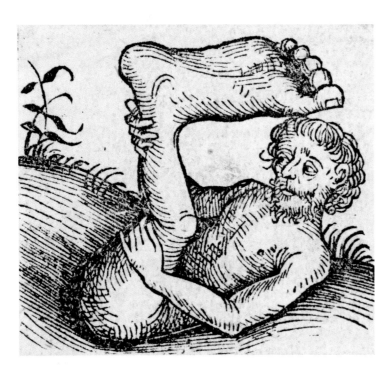

population of blemmyes. In this case euhemerists (those who seek rational explanations for seemingly mythical phenomena) have suggested that the stories may have originated in garbled accounts of wandering Indian ascetics standing on one leg to meditate.

Pliny was a particularly rich source of material on exotic peoples; he also reported hippopodes ("people born with horses' feet") beyond the Carpathian Mountains, while in Africa he recorded the existence of "the Atlas people", a subhuman race who neither dreamed nor called each other by names and who uttered terrible curses at sunrise and sunset, blaming the sun for drying out their fields. Yet he was far from the only one. Reports of strange peoples living beyond the boundaries of normal human contact seem in fact to be an almost universal phenomenon, at least in times when knowledge was limited.

A world of strangeness

Often the stories were of savage races reminiscent of the European woodwose (see page 99). Aborigines in the outback of Australia scared one another with talk of the junjdy, small, hirsute people covered in red fur said to inhabit the mountains on what is now the Queensland–New South Wales border. They were reported to be highly territorial and skilled at hurling spears barbed with the fangs of venomous snakes. On the other side of the world in Alaska, people told similar tales of the urayuli, similarly hairy and unkempt but in their case extremely tall, with long arms reaching down to their ankles. They were peaceful forest-dwellers whose strange, high-pitched cries sometimes broke the silence of the chill Aleutian nights.

The mountains of central Asia have long bred tales of lost tribes with bizarre characteristics. Pliny himself mentioned the Abarimon, who were said to have their feet on backwards yet were marvellously swift runners; their

TALL TALES FROM MAGELLAN'S MEN

One of the most enduring of all travellers' tales concerned a people of unusually tall stature supposed to live in Patagonia at the southern tip of the American continent. Their existence was first reported by Antonio Pigafetta, who accompanied Ferdinand Magellan on the first circumnavigation of the world. He described how, as the expedition coasted southern Argentina, they spotted on shore "a giant, quite naked, who danced, leaped and sang, and while he sang threw sand and dust on his head". Intrigued, Magellan sent a man to make contact with the stranger, instructing him to caper in similar fashion to persuade the native of his good intent. By such means the giant was persuaded to come aboard Magellan's flagship. Subsequently Magellan tricked two other giants into letting themselves be bound in fetters, intending to take them back to Spain to impress his patron, King Charles. In the squalid conditions below decks, the unfortunate captives in fact all died within the year.

Subsequent explorers confirmed Pigafetta's account. For instance, a sailor travelling on Sir Thomas Cavendish's circumnavigation in the 1590s claimed to have seen corpses in the region that were 12 feet (3.65m) long.

It seems likely that the stories were genuine, if sometimes exaggerated, accounts of encounters with the Tehuelche ethnic group, a tall people inhabiting the grasslands of southern Argentina. Sadly, their numbers were cut by Argentinian government campaigns of military expansion in the 1870s; the most recent national census recorded fewer than 6,000 survivors.

homeland was said to be around Mount Imaus in the western Himalayas. Even more famous were the Almas (see page 187), a name that means "wild man" in the Mongolian language. Said to live in the Pamir and Altai ranges of central Asia, they were generally described as naked and hairy but definitely human, unlike the apelike Himalayan yeti. Most accounts made them vaguely Stone Age in appearance, with prominent brows, flat noses and receding chins, and some cryptozoologists have attempted to explain the persistent reports of their existence as evidence of the survival of a relict Neanderthal population in the remote mountain fastnesses of the area.

Extensive distances are not a prerequisite for tales of exotic peoples. Just as Ireland produced a rich folklore detailing an entire secondary population of fairy races (see pages 90–95), so the Hawaiian Islands harboured persistent accounts of rarely-seen tribes hidden in the forests. The Nawao were hunters, and were said to be of larger than normal size. The Menehune, in contrast, were small and were skilled craftsmen, producing splendid canoes, houses and temples. Rather like the Irish Tuatha de Danaan, they were thought of as early inhabitants of the islands who had been displaced by later arrivals, driven into the mountains where they subsisted largely on bananas.

Quetzalcoatl Feathered serpent

Appearance
The plumed serpent of Mesoamerican myth, with the body of a rattlesnake and the feathers of the brightly coloured quetzal bird.

Size
Variable – as a god, Quetzalcoatl could change his shape and size at will.

Lifespan
Immortal.

Powers
Almost unlimited, up to and including the creation of one of the five world-cycles recognized in Aztec cosmology.

Habitat
Mexico and adjoining regions.

Nothing about Quetzalcoatl, the feathered serpent of Aztec lore, is clear cut. As often in Mesoamerican myth, the available evidence is ambiguous. Glimpsed through the surviving sources, he seems a complex, shifting figure with several very different incarnations.

As the feathered serpent, he took the form of a rattlesnake clothed in the scarlet and green plumage of the bird known as the Resplendent quetzal. Several representations show him as a snake with a human head poking out of its mouth, indicating that the god inhabited a serpent's body, or perhaps more accurately chose to take serpentine form.

The whole feathered-serpent image may in fact have begun as a play on words. In the Nahuatl language, the term can also be interpreted to mean "precious twin" – a description referring to one of the god's other avatars, as the Morning Star, Venus. In this guise, Quetzalcoatl was the radiant god of dawn, eternally twinned with Xolotl, the Evening Star.

For the Aztecs Quetzalcoatl was a culture hero who brought maize to the world along with a host of useful arts, among them knowledge of weaving cotton and polishing jade and understanding of the motions of the stars. He was even credited with creating humans in their present form, having descended to the Underworld, to rescue the bones of a previous, departed race of men.

He did so in yet another of his incarnations, as Ehacatl-Quetzalcoatl, god of the winds. In this role he played a major part in Mesoamerican myths, which told of his deadly rivalry with his sibling Tezcatlipoca, "Smoking Mirror", the sinister god of divination and conflict. Each in turn presided over one of the four "suns" or ages of creation that, in the Aztec worldview, preceded the current Fifth Sun. Quetzalcoatl's was the Second Sun, which ended when Tezcatlipoca, in an inversion of the Darwinian order, transformed the people who inhabited it into monkeys. But Quetzalcoatl was later revenged; going down to the Underworld, he stole dead men's bones and dipped them in his own blood to resurrect the human race.

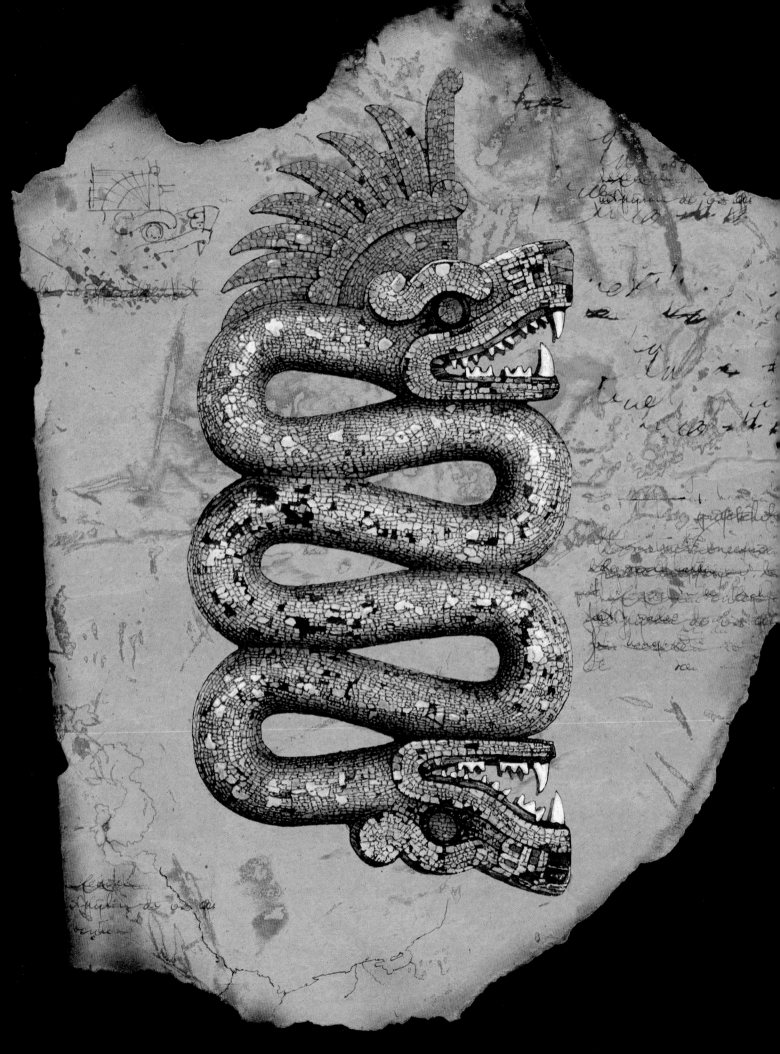

Fenrir Creature of chaos unbound at the world's end

Appearance
Savagely lupine.

Size
Huge, and growing ever larger, eventually to preternatural proportions.

Lifespan
Impossible to kill because fated to survive until Ragnarok (the end of the current cycle of existence).

Powers
Enormous strength and ferocity.

Habitat
Kept bound in Asgard, home of the Norse gods.

In mythology, crossing sexual boundaries often bred monsters. So when the trickster deity Loki chose to mate with the giantess Angrboda – one of a race traditionally hostile to the gods – little good could have been expected of the outcome. Even Loki himself, however, must have been alarmed by the brood that Angrboda bore. Besides the monstrous wolf Fenrir, it comprised the hideous Hel and the world serpent Jormungand (see page 203).

Forewarned that the trio would cause trouble, the Aesir – the reigning deities of Norse myth – sought to neutralize their power. Odin had Jormungand cast into the deepest ocean, where the creature grew to encircle the Earth. Hel, described as half living flesh and half corpse, was dispatched to Niflheim to preside over the land of the dead. That left Fenrir. The gods decided he would be best dealt with by keeping him bound in their own home of Asgard, where they could keep a watchful eye on him.

First, though, he had to be fettered. The gods searched for a material strong enough to hold him. Twice they tried mighty iron chains, challenging the beast to test his strength against them. Each time he tensed his muscles and sent shards of metal flying far and wide.

Odin realized there was only one recourse left: to go to the dwarfs, famous fashioners of magical utensils.

Sure enough, they forged a very different kind of fastening. Gleipnir ("the entangler") was made of the rarest components: a cat's footfall, a woman's beard, a mountain's roots, a bear's sinews, a fish's breath and a bird's spittle. Melded together in the dwarfs' subterranean furnaces, they combined to form a bond no thicker than a silken thread. This, they told Odin, was the tie to hold Fenrir.

No fool, the wolf perceived a trick when confronted with the new challenge. At first he refused point blank to be bound with the thread. But when the Aesir cast aspersions on his strength, he agreed to the test on one condition: that one of the gods should place a hand between his jaws as proof of good faith. No one came forward, and Odin's scheme was on the point of collapsing when finally Tyr, bravest of the Aesir, saved the situation by volunteering. Gleipnir was duly wound round Fenrir's body and legs, and although the wolf struggled with all his might against it, his exertions only made it cling the tighter. Enraged, Fenrir clamped his jaws shut and Tyr lost his hand, cut off at the wrist, known thereafter as the "wolf joint".

Fenrir, however, was at last bound. And so he is destined to remain, not for ever but until the final cataclysm of

> "Gleipnir ('the entangler') was made of the rarest components: a cat's footfall, a woman's beard, a mountain's roots, a bear's sinews, a fish's breath and a bird's spittle."

Ragnarok, which he will help to trigger. For in his days of freedom he sired two offspring, monstrous wolves like himself. One, Skoll, pursues the Sun through the sky each day, hastening it in its course; the other, Hati, chases the Moon. When the predestined time comes round, they will finally catch their prey, plunging the Earth into darkness.

Then the forces of destruction will come together to lay siege to Asgard. Fenrir, grown so vast his upper jaw will reach the heavens, will finally burst his bonds to confront his nemesis Odin, swallowing him up. Yet it is also foretold that Odin's son Vidar will avenge his father, plunging a sword into the wolf-monster's heart and tearing apart his gigantic jaws. Only then, as the present cycle of existence comes to an end in chaos and bloodshed, will the world finally be rid of Fenrir.

Satyr Lustful goatmen of classical groves and forests

When the Greek god of wine Dionysus went abroad, he did so accompanied by a train of satyrs. Like centaurs (see pages 122–125), these untamed nature spirits were halfway between men and beasts, marked by animal appetites that in Freudian terms were all id uninhibited by any superego. One of their ilk, the demigod Silenus, had been Dionysus's tutor. Elderly satyrs were in fact referred to as silenes, and were portrayed as fat and wise but generally even more drunken than their youthful counterparts.

In early classical art satyrs were shown as primarily human, but from the fourth century BCE on they became animals from the waist down, perhaps under the influence of Roman fauns (see box, opposite). Usually the animal was a goat, but they were also often shown with horses' tails and hooves. Satyrs were a favourite theme in the art of the Renaissance. The late fifteenth-century

painting by the Florentine artist Piero di Cosimo, shown below, depicts a satyr with typically caprine hindquarters mourning over a nymph.

Compulsive womanizers

The tenderness of Piero's depiction was unusual, however, for if satyrs had a single dominant characteristic, it was their insatiable sexual appetite. According to Pliny, their very name derived from a Greek term for the virile member. They were never happier than when chasing nymphs; the modern term "satyriasis", used to describe compulsive womanizing, recalls their predilections. As such, they were worshipped as spirits of fertility, and country people in ancient Greece offered up lambs and the first fruits of the harvest in their honour.

In medieval times classical accounts of their hybrid form and high-spirited behaviour caused bestiarists to confuse them with newly discovered varieties of monkeys. Even into the Age of Reason, the pioneering taxonomist Linnaeus chose *Simia satyrus* as the original scientific name for the orang-utan (now known as *Pongo pygmaeus*). Memories of them live on in modern Greece in stories of the Christmas goblins called kallikantzaroi, pictured like the satyrs with pointed ears, goat legs and a passion for dancing.

Appearance
Goats from the waist down, their heads and upper bodies were those of human males.

Size
Approximately human.

Lifespan
Lengthy but not immortal.

Powers
Spirits of untamed nature, they were renowned for their unquenchable sexual appetites and capacity for drink, but also for their cowardice in fleeing danger.

Habitat
Forests and groves of the classical world.

141

FOLLOWERS OF FAUNUS

The Roman equivalent of satyrs were the fauns, followers and devotees of the pastoral god Faunus. Satyrs may in fact owe their goatlike appearance to the god, who was normally portrayed with goat legs and horns. Besides being a fertility deity of flocks and crops, Faunus was also associated with oracular dreams, revealed to individuals who consulted him in sacred groves. The fauns who accompanied him were gentler in temperament than their Greek counterparts and less given to drunkenness and riot.

In recent times C.S. Lewis featured a faun in *The Lion, The Witch and The Wardrobe*; named Tumnus, he is the first creature Lucy meets on her arrival in Narnia, signalling that she has entered a magic land. Originally intending to deliver her to the evil White Witch, Tumnus has a change of heart and eventually guides Lucy back to the earthly realm.

Yuki-onna Japan's beautiful spirit of the snows

Appearance
A beautiful, white-complexioned woman, sometimes also clothed in white, although on other occasions she appears naked.

Size
Ordinary human scale.

Lifespan
Immortal.

Powers
Can kill with a touch or a breath.

Habitat
Japan's mountains and wild places; only seen in winter.

Travellers crossing a mountain range somewhere in Japan encounter unexpectedly harsh weather conditions. The mist closes in, and before long they are stranded in a white-out, unable to see the path more than a few yards ahead of them. Then snow starts to fall. Before long a full-scale blizzard is raging.

In the eerie silence of the snowfall, they find themselves marooned, trapped between Earth and Heaven in a lethal white cocoon. As the temperature plunges, a terrible lethargy descends upon them. Unable to save themselves, they wait, helpless and hopeless. Then, just as consciousness is drifting away, a figure emerges from the swirling snow. A beautiful woman glides soundlessly toward them, her complexion as white as the silk kimono wrapped about her. Her face is calm and peaceful, but it is also resolute. She is the spirit of the snows, come to clasp them in her icy embrace. When the storm finally passes, only their lifeless bodies will remain, slumped where they halted. Their spirits have gone with the snow maiden, lost forever to the icy fastnesses that she inhabits.

The great Japanese film-maker Akira Kurosawa pictured the scene in his last film, *Dreams*. Western audiences mostly found the episode surrealistic, but in fact he was portraying the snow woman Yuki-onna, a well-established figure in Japanese legend. She is one of the best known of the *yokai* or spirits, whose ranks also include the kitsune (see pages 118–119) and the tengu (see pages 40–41). Once seen as purely evil, she is now more often viewed as an ambivalent figure, as in Kurosawa's depiction, with an otherworldly glamour that belies her lethal intent.

Minokichi's promise

Sometimes Yuki-onna can even show pity. One of the best-known tales about her is that recounted in Lafcadio Hearn's English-language classic *Kwaidan*. It tells of two woodcutters caught in an unheated hut in the midst of a blizzard. The older one died, but his young apprentice, Minokichi, survived, having glimpsed an apparition of a beautiful woman stooping protectively over him. He heard, or thought he heard, her whispering that she would preserve him so long as he never mentioned to any living soul what he had seen that night.

Not long afterward, the young man met a stranger on the little-frequented path that he took each day to the forest. She was a girl of his own age with long black hair framing an unusually pale face, travelling to stay with distant relatives. It took little to persuade her to break her journey at the home he shared with his mother. She never left, and soon the two were married.

The couple were happy, and brought up several children. Then one evening when they were resting in their warm house with a cold wind blowing outside, Minokichi found himself recalling his ordeal in the hut many years earlier, before he met his partner. Unthinkingly, he started to tell her the story, only to find himself rudely interrupted.

"You promised never to tell a living soul," his normally placid spouse spat out in a terrible voice he had never heard her use before. "I am Yuki-onna, and now I must leave you. I shall spare you once more, for our children's sake; but if you should ever mistreat them, even unintentionally, you shall not live to see another day, or another minute." And with that his spirit-bride was gone, never to be seen or heard of any more.

Wendigo Icy-hearted horror within the Canadian forests

Appearance
Invariably horrible, although accounts vary on the details. Recurring features include sharp, jagged teeth, lips (and sometimes a tongue) that seem to have been chewed off by animals, a skeletal frame, and badly deformed feet missing several toes.

Size
Variable, for the wendigo could change dimension, from small to preternaturally huge.

Lifespan
The wendigo could not normally be killed, although some reports claimed it could be destroyed by melting its heart of ice.

Powers
Shape-shifting powers and cannibalistic appetites, combined with the ability to move at great speed on land and in the air.

Habitat
The great forests of Canada.

The forests of Canada are among the world's last great wilderness areas, and their expanses have spawned legends to match the fears their silent vastness inspires. The Algonquian-speaking peoples of eastern North America told tales of the wendigo, a forest spirit that embodied all the terrors lone travellers could feel in a landscape laid out on a more-than-human scale. Anyone who has travelled through woods with the feeling that something terrible is tracking them knows something of the paranoia that the being could inspire.

Over the years, different versions of the tradition developed. Some storytellers claimed there was only one wendigo, while others held there were many. By general consent, the creature was a prodigious shape-shifter.

The principal features attributed to it were all in some way linked to the primal fears raised by the forest. It was said to have a heart of ice, symbolizing the pitilessness of the great woods, not caring whether a lone hunter lived or died. Its body was described as skeletal, calling up the spectre of starvation that

was never far away in winter. People said its feet lacked toes, suggesting frostbite, while its lips were eaten away like those of corpses left to the scavengers of the forest. Above all it was cannibalistic, summoning up the greatest taboo of all: that which prevented small communities in the extremities of hunger from devouring their own kind.

Worse than death

Some people thought that shamans could transform their enemies into the monsters. Others insisted that outcasts who for whatever reason indulged in cannibalism became wendigos even if they did not start in that condition. Yet the greatest fear of all was of being hunted down by an existing wendigo, for, like vampires, the beings had the power to create victims in their own image. There were several ways in which that disaster might happen. A traveller might chance upon one in the forest, or even accidentally cross its track. More terrifyingly still, a hunter might himself become hunted, pursued through the woods for hours or even days by an unseen stalker.

Wendigos could even shadow their victims in their sleep, dreams being powerful channels of psychic energy in the Native American worldview.

Whatever the form of contact, the fate of the victims was always terrible. In some stories they were devoured by the wendigo and were seen no more. In others they were paralysed by fear until their hearts stopped or they froze to death. Most often, though, they themselves became wendigos, and that was the worst outcome of all. For the victims usually retained enough of their former consciousness to know what was happening to them; and in moments when they were in their right minds, their only wish was to die, to be put out of their eternal misery.

Such fears were far from idle fancies. Trapped in the long northern winters, some individuals went mad with the fear of turning into a wendigo. Others found themselves gripped by an insane craving for human flesh. The condition was even dignified with a scientific name: wendigo psychosis.

It was, in fact, just such a case that brought knowledge of the wendigo from the Canadian woodlands to the wider world. Early in the twentieth century Algernon Blackwood, a well-known English writer of supernatural stories, was living in a backwoods region of Canada where he chanced to hear of a man in the grip of the condition. He used the material as the inspiration for a story, *The Wendigo*, which in time became a horror classic. It was largely thanks to his work that the creature took its place in the darker recesses of the world's imagination, joining its better-known peers, the vampire and the werewolf.

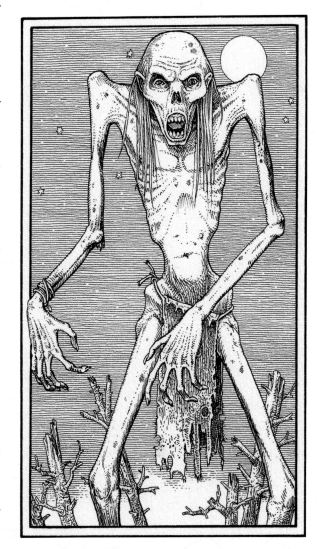

Banshee Wailing harbinger of death

Appearance
Fairy women usually seen weeping and distraught and dressed in white or grey.

Size
Human-sized, although often described as tall.

Lifespan
As fairies, unaffected by the passing of time or age.

Powers
The ability to predict death.

Habitat
Ireland. The Scottish equivalent was the *bean nighe* ("washerwoman").

Banshees were among the most distinctive of the multifarious Irish fairy folk. The word literally meant "woman of the *sidhe*" – the *sidhe* being the fairy race that shared the island of Erin with its human inhabitants. Said to be a relict population driven underground by the arrival of the present occupants, they were thought to live under hills and hummocks, the fairy mounds of Celtic legend.

Banshees were harbingers of death who took the form of women – often beautiful ones. No one who heard it ever forgot their terrible cry, a wailing scream that denoted imminent bereavement. The keening of peasant women at Irish wakes was said to be a pale imitation of the sound.

One possible origin for the tales may have been memories of the Washer at the Ford. Sometimes portrayed as a young girl and sometimes as a wizened hag, she featured in Celtic myth as a prophetess of doom, seen scrubbing blood-stained garments by warriors on their way to battle. If one stopped to ask what she was doing, she usually replied ominously that it was his clothes that she was washing.

The tradition of keening may itself have contributed to the legend. It was said that, while ordinary mortals had human mourners to grieve for them, members

---

THE ERL KING

The German equivalent of the banshee was the erl king, best known from Goethe's ballad of the same name (*Der Erlkönig*), which was famously set to music by Franz Schubert. Although the word literally means "king of the alder trees", it is generally thought to have originated in a mistranslation of the term "elf king". Unlike his Irish counterpart, the German erl king not only portended death but actively enticed people to embrace it. In the Goethe poem, the erl king's child victim could hear his blandishments, promising all the delights of the Otherworld. Yet the boy's uncomprehending father rode on regardless, only to arrive home to find his son lifeless behind him in the saddle.

of the five great Gaelic families of Ireland – the Kavanaghs, O'Briens, O'Connors, O'Neills and O'Gradys – were lamented by the *sidhe*. In this way a certain snobbery came to attach itself to the spectral mourners, caught in Clarence Mangan's lines: "Not for churls with souls like hucksters/Waileth our Banshee!"

Over time the legends became confused with stories of the dullahan, another Irish messenger of death. Bearing his head under his arm and riding a headless horse, he was a figure of fantasy dear to the hearts of generations of storytellers. At their most baroque, their accounts of deaths foretold featured not just a wailing banshee but also a black coach bearing a coffin, steered by a dullahan and his decapitated steeds.

Yet the most striking tales were generally the simpler ones. The poet W.B. Yeats recorded a classic encounter. A mother and her daughters had been summoned to a house in southern Ireland where a death was expected. As they approached their destination by night, they suddenly heard from behind a hedge a terrible scream. "If it resembled anything earthly," one daughter wrote, "it seemed the cry of a female, struck by a sudden and mortal blow, and giving out her life in one long, deep pang of expiring agony". Through a gap in the

hedge they caught a moonlit glimpse of the figure from whom the sound had come, described as "a tall, thin woman with uncovered head and long hair that floated round her shoulders, attired in something which seemed either a loose white cloak or a sheet thrown hastily about her". When they arrived at the house soon after, they found the son of the family dead.

Werewolves Humans transformed into wolves

Appearance
Wolflike. Usually the transformation was complete, with the affected humans in effect becoming wolves; occasionally it was partial, with only some features altered.

Size
Between wolf and human.

Lifespan
The werewolf condition was usually transitory, sometimes passing after a fixed time, such as nine years.

148

Powers
Shape-shifting abilities. Most werewolves showed ferocity and a taste for human flesh, although those unwillingly transformed could be harmless and even gentle.

Habitat
Almost all countries where wolves were known.

Almost every culture had stories of individuals with the ability to transform themselves or other people into animals. The most widespread legends spoke of werewolves, although lands that had no wolves had similar tales attached to other predators; so there were weretigers in India, wereleopards in Africa and werejaguars in South America (see pages 152–153).

The tales went back a long way. In the European tradition they can be traced back as far as the fifth-century BCE Greek traveller and historian Herodotus, who reported that a tribe called the Neuri, living beyond the borders of Scythia in what is now Poland, were said to change into wolves once a year, remaining in that condition for days on end. Herodotus himself was sceptical of the story, which may have reflected shamanistic practices involving the donning of wolf skins for religious rites.

Greek mythology also recounted the story of Lycaon, the first king of Arcadia, who sacrificed a human child to Zeus

THE BEAST OF GÉVAUDAN

Between 1764 and 1767 a man-eating wolf terrorized the wild Gévaudan region of France, now within the Lozère *département* in the southern Massif Central. By all accounts it killed a large number of people – most accounts list between sixty and a hundred dead. Most of its victims were children and girls, particularly – to quote Robert Louis Stevenson, who reported the story in *Travels with a Donkey in the Cévennes* – "shepherdesses noted for their beauty". Eventually its depradations came to the attention of King Louis XV himself, who sent royal huntsmen to track it down. They duly killed a large wolf, but not the right one, for the attacks continued. They only stopped when a local hunter, Jean Chastel, killed another animal some eighteen months later. The beast's predilection for human victims, even when cattle were nearby in the same field, coupled with one report that it was seen crossing a stream on its hind legs, have led to suggestions that some of the attacks might have been the work of a werewolf or, more likely, of a serial killer disguised in wolf's clothing.

and in punishment was turned into a wolf; in another version of the story, he and his fifty sons served Zeus a soup made with human entrails, and were all so transformed. Elaborations of the tale also claimed that whenever sacrifices were subsequently made on Lycaon's altar, one of the officiants turned into a wolf, reverting to human form after nine years only if he refrained from ever tasting human flesh.

Wolf-men of ancient Rome

Stories of werewolves were also widespread in Roman times. Pliny the Elder was unconvinced, commenting "I can state with confidence that the assertion that men can be turned into wolves and back again is false; believe that, and we must also believe all the other tales that over so many generations have turned out to be fabulous."

The Roman author Petronius Arbiter, writing in the first century CE, included a classic werewolf tale in his *Satyricon*. One of the characters tells banquet guests how, travelling to visit a girlfriend, he

fell in with a soldier who, under a full moon, stripped off all his clothes then urinated in a circle around them, turning them hard as stone. The stranger then took wolf shape and loped off into the night. Arriving at his lover's farm, the traveller learned that a wolf had attacked her flocks only to be driven

CLINICAL LYCANTHROPY

Modern psychiatry recognizes a rare condition in which affected individuals believe themselves to be changing (or to have been transformed) into animals. Wolves often feature in this form of psychosis, although individuals have also reported turning into dogs, horses, birds, tigers and even frogs. The condition has been recorded in widely scattered parts of the world, including India and Ethiopia, where it was traditionally dealt with by exorcism.

A recent neuro-imaging study of two affected individuals revealed unusual levels of activity in parts of the brain involved in the conceptualization of body image – the subjects of the research actually perceived their bodies to be changing shape – suggesting that there may be some neurological basis for the state, however much it might also be affected by specific cultural factors.

off with a spear thrust to the neck. Returning home next day, he discovered the soldier, back in human form, being treated by doctors for a similarly located wound.

A world of superstitions

Stories of this kind would be told in many different lands over the next two millennia. They varied in their details, particularly over the way in which people ended up as werewolves. Some were bewitched by sorcerers, and these were often tragic figures, haunting their old abodes and pitifully seeking help from their former acquaintances. Others were predisposed to the condition, perhaps because they were conceived out of wedlock, or else born on Christmas Eve, or had unusually hairy hands or eyebrows that met over their nose. In northern Argentina the belief that seventh sons were fated to become werewolves gained such a hold that infants were sometimes abandoned or even killed by their parents to avoid the fate. To combat the practice, President Hipólito Yrigoyen decreed in 1920 that he would serve as godfather to all seventh sons, a tradition that survives to the present day.

Other people chose to transform themselves into wolves, a feat typically accomplished by rubbing themselves with a magic salve or donning a wolfskin girdle. In wolf form such individuals were almost invariably predatory, seeking out humans to kill and eat. Usually they were nocturnal, being forced to return to human form by daybreak. There were many ways of countering their magic, some as simple as showing the sign of the cross or calling out their baptismal name three times aloud. In other traditions, though, they were hard to kill, being impervious to weapons unless they had been blessed in a chapel sacred to St Hubert, patron saint of huntsmen. In more recent times, the weapon of choice for those seeking to kill a werewolf has been a firearm loaded with silver bullets.

Lupine lawbreakers

For a time between the fourteenth and sixteenth centuries werewolves moved out of legend to become serious objects of legal concern in Europe. The trigger was a council of the Church, summoned by the Holy Roman Emperor Sigismund, that decreed that werewolves really existed. As a result there was a marked increase in reports of werewolf behaviour. The Swedish ecclesiast and historian Olaus Magnus reported the existence of a regular coven in the eastern Baltic region, supposedly involving "the great men and chiefest nobility of the land". These individuals would come together on Christmas night and take wolf form by reciting a magic formula over a cup of ale. They would then break into people's homes to commit murder and mayhem, but could be easily distinguished from real wolves because they also broke open beer barrels during their rampages.

In the late sixteenth century France experienced a rash of trials of supposed werewolves. Some of the accused seem to have been serial killers, sometimes with a taste for cannibalism. Others were no doubt entirely innocent. One case occurring in Riom, near Clermont-Ferrand, in 1588 involved a woman of rank who supposedly attacked a game-keeper while in wolf form. He fought the animal off with difficulty, cutting off one of its paws. By the time he showed the trophy to his master, it had report-edly reverted to human shape, and the landowner recognized with horror his own wife's hand, identifiable from the ring – a family heirloom – on one finger. Like most of those found guilty of lycan-thropy, the woman was subsequently burned at the stake.

"Others were predisposed to the condition, perhaps because they were conceived out of wedlock, or else born on Christmas Eve, or had unusually hairy hands."

151

Cat Creatures Werecats and feline deities

Appearance
Feline, and most often (but not always) female. The folklore of nations around the world has tales of people turning into a variety of different species, including most of the big cats.

Size
Usually the normal dimensions of the species involved. Some accounts of transformations, though, described human-sized domestic cats that walked on their hindlegs.

Lifespan
Variable.

Powers
The ability to shift shape between human and animal form.

Habitat
Known wherever cats have traditionally been found, on every continent except Antarctica and Australia.

152

The best-known cat creature in the West today is also one of the least typical. Catwoman was of course a fictional character, created for D.C. Comics by Bob Kane, the inventor of Batman, and his collaborator Bill Finger. She first appeared in the original *Batman* comic, published in 1940, as an adversary of the eponymous caped hero. Kane seems to have taken his inspiration from the phrase "cat burglar", because the original Catwoman was a thief, marked out above all by her agility. Subsequent reinterpretations, notably in the 1992 film *Batman Returns*, have retained her criminality, but given the character a feminist twist as a symbol of female power.

One of the most significant things about Catwoman was her gender, for cat people tended to be female, just as werewolves were generally male. Such was the case with the witch's familiar. Although other animals turned up from time to time in court records, familiars were generally feline, sometimes changing shape with their mistresses. Cats featured in evidence in many of the witch trials that disgraced sixteenth- and seventeenth-century Europe, and false claims about harmless pets no doubt helped send many innocent women to the stake. In France cats suspected of being familiars were sometimes caged or even burned alive.

Lingering suspicions of demonic connections no doubt fed into superstitions about cats bringing ill luck. Some people refused to speak of intimate family matters with a stray cat in the room in case it should turn out to be a familiar, while in eastern Europe domestic cats were sometimes marked with a cross to prevent them from turning into witches.

Yet an alternative tradition saw cats rather as bringers of good fortune. This positive view has a pedigree at least as long as the satanic-familiar image. It can be traced all the way back to ancient Egypt, where domestic cats were much-loved pets, cherished both as mousers and as adversaries of snakes, a household bane. The sun god Ra even had an ally, the Great Cat of Heliopolis, that helped guard him from the chaos serpent Apep (see page 196), who waited to ambush him on his daily journey across the sky.

The best-known Egyptian cat goddess was Bastet, a daughter of Ra. In early times she was depicted with a lion's head and was associated with war and vengeance. Later, however, she surrendered that role to her sister Sekhmet, also lion-headed, a war goddess from Upper Egypt. Instead, Bastet became cat-faced and was affectionately venerated as the guardian and protector of domestic felines.

The Greek traveller Herodotus described the raucous scenes attending her festival, held in the town of Bubastis, 50 miles (80km) northeast of modern Cairo. Supposedly the festivities drew more than 700,000 visitors annually. People would travel to the centre by barge along the Nile, singing, clapping hands and shaking the rattle-like instruments known as *sistra*. When they passed by towns, they would steer close to the bank, and the women would dance, shout playful abuse at the passers-by, and even suggestively hitch up their skirts.

Although almost as venerable as their Egyptian counterparts, the feline gods of Mesoamerica were much more sinister. The Olmecs, who created the first known organized culture in the region, carved statuettes of a cryptic figure – a plump baby, distinguished from his normal human counterparts by cat's ears and feral fangs, and sometimes also by the

stylized marking of a big cat's pawprint on his forehead. Although the Olmecs left no written records to document their customs, archaeologists believe that the children were thought of in effect as werejaguars, born of the mating of a jaguar and a woman. These predatory infants, who may have been venerated as divine ancestors of the Olmec race, could take the shape of either of their parents, combining both human intelligence and the jaguar's power.

Gorgons Hideous, snake-haired sisters

Appearance
Figures of fear, with sharp fangs, protruding tongues, bronze claws, and snakes for hair.

Size
Slightly larger than life.

Lifespan
Of the three Gorgons, two were immortal. Medusa was not, for the hero Perseus killed her.

Powers
Faces so hideous that they could turn all who saw them to stone.

Habitat
On the farther side of the Western Ocean, near the Garden of the Hesperides. In later years, tradition claimed that their home was in Libya.

Across ancient Greece, people chose to adorn doors, city walls, breastplates and even tombstones with a figure of pure horror. They called the symbol the *gorgoneion*, and it was so terrible that it was held to ward off evil. People wore it on amulets to protect themselves from the evil eye. According to Homer, King Agamemnon, leader of the Greek army before Troy, had it emblazoned on his shield. Even Zeus was said to bear its image on the aegis, his magical buckler.

The *gorgoneion* represented a face from nightmares, wreathed with snakes in place of hair. The original was said to be so ghastly that it turned all who looked at it to stone. In the earliest myths it was the visage of a single being, born of the earth goddess Gaia to aid her sons the giants in their battle against the gods. Later, though, there were three Gorgons: Stheno (the Mighty), Euryale (the Far-Springer), and Medusa (the Queen).

Legend claimed that Medusa, unlike her terrible sisters, had been born beautiful – causing the sea god Poseidon to lust after her and, indeed, violate her in a temple sacred to Athene. Infuriated

at the impiety, the goddess took her revenge by turning the girl's golden locks into writhing serpents.

It was Medusa that the hero Perseus vowed to slay, and with divine aid he was able to do so by beheading her as she slept, taking care that he saw only her reflected image in his mirrored shield. From the wound two fabulous creatures sprang forth: the winged horse Pegasus and the giant Chrysaor. The severed head retained its lethal power, and Perseus was later able to use it as a weapon to petrify the tyrant Polydectes, who had originally sent him on his dangerous quest.

Others of Medusa's bodyparts, however, had restorative powers. While blood taken from the right-hand side of her body was fatally envenomed, that from the left had healing properties – so powerful that it could even bring the dead back to life. The goddess Athene gave some drops to the healer Asclepius, who used them to revivify corpses, causing Hades to complain to Zeus that his subjects were being stolen from him – a problem Zeus quickly rectified by striking Asclepius down with a thunderbolt.

Cerberus & Orthrus Multi-headed dogs of myth

Appearance
Fearsome canine siblings. Orthrus had two heads and Cerberus three, plus a mane of serpents' heads and a snake for a tail.

Size
Huge, but not so big as to prevent Hercules from seizing Cerberus in an armlock.

Lifespan
Evidently not immortal, as Hercules killed Orthrus.

Powers
Great power and ferocity and, in Cerberus's case, the ability to prevent souls from leaving the Underworld as well as barring living things from entering it.

Habitat
Cerberus guarded the gates of the classical Underworld. Orthrus lived on the island of Erytheia ("Red Island"), beyond the Pillars of Hercules in the stream of Ocean – in other words, somewhere in the Atlantic.

Brothers to the chimera and the Lernaean hydra, Cerberus and Orthrus were part of the dreadful brood born in classical myth to Typhon and Echidna. Both were dogs, but unlike any others the world had ever seen: Cerberus had three heads, Orthrus two.

Cerberus's task was to guard the entrance to the Underworld. There he had the dual responsibility of preventing the living from entering while also stopping the souls of the dead from slipping back to the human world. New arrivals had to find a way past him if they were to win a place in Hades' kingdom, and to help them do so grieving relatives took care to bury them with honey-cakes. The cakes served as the legendary "sops to Cerberus", thrown to distract the dog's attention as the souls scurried past.

Trickery and artistry

Classical myth had several tales of intrepid individuals who found ways of outwitting Cerberus while still alive. In Virgil's epic *The Aeneid*, the Cumaean Sibyl laced a honey-cake with opiates to drug the guard-dog, permitting her

---

GARM — THE HOUND OF HELL

The Norse world had a close equivalent of Cerberus in Garm, the dog that guarded the entry to Niflheim, where Hel, goddess of death, dwelled. Souls headed for that dreadful land faced a long, cold journey to the far north. At the end of many days' travelling, they came to the icy waters of the Gjöll stream, spanned by a crystal bridge that was suspended by a single hair. To cross it, they had to pay a tithe of blood to its skeletal female guardian, Modgud. On the other side of the river the track passed through Ironwood, a forest of bare, metallic trees, before reaching the gate of Hel's kingdom, where Garm lurked in the Gnipa cave.

And so he is destined to remain until Ragnarok, the end of the present age. In that final, epic confrontation, he will at last be freed to join the hosts of chaos, only to meet his end fighting to the death with Tyr, bravest of all the Norse gods.

to smuggle the hero Aeneas past his den. Psyche used a similar trick on her way to the Underworld on a mission to regain Cupid's love. Orpheus, in contrast, relied solely on the soothing power of his music to calm Cerberus when he travelled there to regain his lost wife Eurydice.

Journey to the land of the living

Cerberus's principal role in classical myth was, however, as the target of the last of the twelve labours set for Hercules by King Eurystheus of Tiryns, which was to venture down to the Underworld and bring Cerberus back alive. Hercules wisely secured Hades' permission before attempting the feat, but only on condition that he master the beast without the use of weapons – a feat he accomplished by seizing the dog in an armlock while relying on his impenetrable lionskin tunic to protect him from the snakes on its mane and tail. As the hero led his prey up to the land of the living, foam from the monster's slavering jaws congealed to create venomous aconite plants. Eurystheus was so terrified by the sight of the dog

that he leaped for safety into a vast storage jar. Hercules subsequently returned Cerberus to Hades unharmed.

The seizing of Geryon's cattle

Orthrus also featured in the Hercules cycle of legends, in his case in the tenth labour: the seizing of Geryon's cattle. Geryon was a giant with triple torsos who lived on an island in the mysterious far west. To guard his famous, red-shanked cattle he relied on a herdsman, Eurytion, who kept Orthrus as a guard-dog. The hero duly dispatched the two of them with his club before killing Geryon himself with a single arrow that penetrated all of his three bodies in a single shot.

157

Vampires Undead beings who crave blood

Appearance
Of any age and either gender. Typically thin and pale-complexioned, except after drinking blood.

Size
Human.

Lifespan
Undead, vampires were compelled to remain so until finally laid to rest by human or divine intervention.

Powers
The ability to rise from the grave and wander abroad at night in search of blood. Their victims became vampires in their turn.

Habitat
Vampire-like beings have been reported from many parts of the world, but the heartland of vampire legend was the Slavic countries and adjoining eastern European lands.

In 1725 a peasant named Peter Plogojowitz passed away in his home village of Kisiljevo, near Serbia's modern-day border with Romania. A couple of months later nine other villagers died within the space of a week. Before their deaths each one claimed to have been visited in his or her sleep by the dead man, who seemed to throttle the life out of them. Plogojowitz's wife also received a visit, whereupon she fled the district.

News of the events in Kisiljevo (then known as Kisilova) reached the Habsburg authorities, who ruled the region at the time as part of the Austro–Hungarian Empire. The local district commissioner was duly dispatched to investigate the deaths. Against his wishes the terrified villagers insisted on exhuming Plogojowitz's body in his presence. In the report he subsequently prepared on the incident, he noted that: "The body, except for the nose, which was somewhat decomposed, was completely fresh … . With some astonishment I noticed some fresh blood on his mouth, which, according to the generally held view, he had sucked from the people he had killed."

The discovery seemed to confirm the villagers' worst fears. Plogojowitz had become a vampire – a restless spirit caught between the realms of the living and the dead who could subsist only on a diet of human blood. His body was duly dealt with in the traditional way. A sharpened stake was driven through its heart, causing fresh blood to spurt from the chest, ears and mouth, and the corpse was then burned to ashes.

Parallel traditions

The Serbians were not alone in believing in the undead. Lands around the world had tales of similar, bloodthirsty spirits. In Surinam on South America's Atlantic coast, women called azemans were said to turn into animals by night to drink human blood. China had its *jiangshi*, "hopping corpses", restless spirits that killed people so they could then steal their *qi*, or vital essence.

Yet it was in eastern Europe that the classic vampire tradition grew to fruition. Even the English word derives from the

region, traced alternatively from the Hungarian or Serbo-Croat *vampir*.

It was in those two countries that vampire hysteria reached a peak in the eighteenth century, rivalling the witchcraft mania that had swept western Europe a couple of hundred years earlier. Most of what is known of the scare comes from the dispatches of Habsburg officials like the Kisiljevo commissioner. The best-documented case concerned one Arnold Paole, a former irregular soldier who broke his neck in a farming accident and was held responsible for subsequently causing the death of more than twenty people in his native village of Medvedja in southern Serbia. Five army officers, one a surgeon, were sent to investigate. In all they exhumed seventeen bodies. Five showed signs of decomposition, but the other twelve were all undecayed and had fresh blood in their chests. The corpses were subsequently decapitated and burned.

The officers' report, along with similar documents, were widely circulated at the time, helping to spread word of vampires, previously familiar only to eastern European peasants, to the rest of the continent. A French Benedictine monk, Dom Augustin Calmet, published a scholarly tract of the phenomenon in 1746, giving the vampire some intellectual respectability.

The voice of reason

Yet the eighteenth century was the Age of Reason, and sceptical voices were quickly raised to pour scorn on the stories. When a fresh case came to light in Moravia in 1755, Empress Maria Theresa, herself an Enlightenment figure, sent her personal physician to observe the events. He produced a damning report, pointing out that one supposed female vampire, buried in December and dug up in January, showed no signs of decomposition simply because her body had been deep-frozen. He explained away other apparently fresh bodies in terms of dry earth and tightly packed coffins. (Modern scientific investigators also point out that ruddiness and uncoagulated blood are both normally found in corpses at certain stages of the

"The title character of the novella was based on Byron himself, helping set a fictional fashion for refined, aristocratic bloodsuckers that was to endure for more than a century."

decomposition process.) The empress subsequently passed a decree forbidding the opening of graves and the desecration of corpses.

Maria Theresa's action effectively put an end to the vampire mania in eastern Europe. Soon after, though, tales of vampirism found a new lease of life, this time in western European literature. The poet Lord Byron touched on the subject in his poem *The Giaour*, and John Polidori, his personal physician, published *The Vampyre*, soon after. The title character of the novella was based on Byron himself, helping set a fictional fashion for refined, aristocratic bloodsuckers that was to endure for more than a century.

Serial penny dreadfuls like *Varney the Vampire* helped keep the theme alive in the mid-nineteenth century, while Sheridan LeFanu brought lesbian undertones to *Carmilla*, published in 1872. The undisputed classic of the genre, however, was Bram Stoker's *Dracula*, which first saw the light of day in 1897, firmly entrenching vampire lore in the popular imagination. In the twentieth century the cinema took up the baton, from F.W. Murnau's silent classic *Nosferatu*, released in 1922, to *Buffy the Vampire Slayer*, a 1992 cinema release aimed at the teen market that

subsequently spawned a hugely successful television series.

By that time most Western adolescents were growing up as familiar with vampire lore as any eighteenth-century Transylvanian peasant. Some new elements had been introduced in the interim, among them the idea of vampires transforming into bats (thought to have been Bram Stoker's invention) and the notion that they cast no shadow. Yet the basic concept of the undead surviving on a diet of human blood remained unchanged. The vampire may have faded from the world of belief, but it still flourishes in the realm of the imagination.

BLOODSUCKERS OF SOUTHEAST ASIA

Southeast Asian legend described various ghoulish creatures generically known as aswangs (see pages 65–66), of which some had characteristics strikingly reminiscent of eastern European vampires. The manananggaal of the Philippines was a beautiful woman whose upper torso could magically detach itself at night and fly off on batlike wings in search of victims – generally pregnant women asleep in their beds. When it found a suitable prey, the creature sucked out her blood – or the heart of the foetus – transforming the pregnant woman in her turn into a manananggaal. Like vampires, manananggaals hated the scent of garlic.

Similar legends in Malaysia spoke of the pontianak, the undead spirits of women who had died in childbirth, who were said to roam the neighbourhood where they had lived in search of victims. Well-prepared individuals carried an iron nail to plunge into the back of the pontianak's neck in case of attack, thereby turning it back from vampire to human form.

Chupacabra Blood-sucking predator or modern myth?

Appearance
Accounts vary. Some describe a creature that hops like a kangaroo, with a doglike head and a body that may be either scaly or coarsely furred. Others report a hairless wild dog with prominent eye sockets and a pronounced spinal ridge.

Size
Typically 3ft (1m) tall or more.

Lifespan
Unknown.

Powers
A taste for sucking blood, seemingly through its fangs. Some reports speak of hypnotic red eyes that mesmerize the beast's prey.

Habitat
The Caribbean islands of Puerto Rico and Hispaniola, and central regions of the American mainland from Chile to Maine.

In the early 1990s reports began to radiate out of the Caribbean island of Puerto Rico of a rash of animal deaths. The strangest feature of the attacks was that the victims seemed to have been sucked dry of blood. Each one was also said to have puncture marks on its neck, seemingly caused by fangs.

The stories recalled an earlier incident on the island, when in 1975 a number of unexplained deaths of animals around the small town of Moca had led to newspaper stories about the "Moca vampire". UFOlogists claimed at the time that the killings were linked with strange objects seen in the sky. Speculation flared that the beasts were falling prey to aliens, if not to human Satanists wandering the island in search of sacrificial victims.

The earlier wave of stories petered out when the killings stopped, but the 1990s tales showed greater longevity. A local television personality nicknamed the perpetrators chupacabras ("goatsuckers") and the tag stuck. Soon reports of related animal deaths started flowing in from the neighbouring Dominican Republic and then from the American mainland.

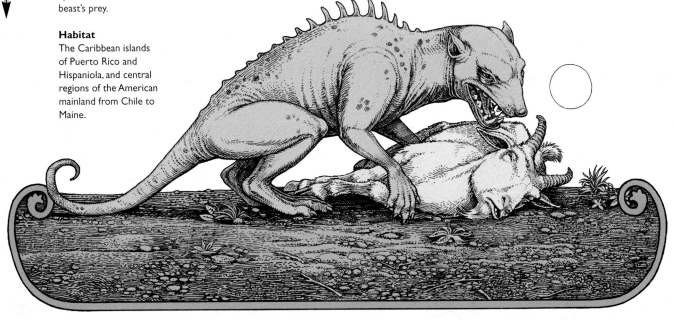

Over the next decade chupacabra attacks were reported from as far afield as Chile and Maine, on animals ranging from chickens and turkeys through pet cats and dogs to cattle, sheep and, as the name would suggest, goats.

Soon reports of sightings began to circulate. The early stories were spectacular, speaking of a creature with scaly skin, a doglike head, a forked tongue and glowing red eyes that stood on two legs and hopped like a kangaroo. About 3 feet (1m) high, the chupacabra had a row of sharp quills running down its back. When the beast took to flight, it left a foul, sulphurous odour behind.

Alien or mammalian?

Among the many oddities of the description was the sheer blend of elements involved. The scaly skin and forked tongue seemed reptilian, while the hopping motion inevitably recalled Australian marsupials. The doglike head, however, sounded mammalian. Attempts to explain the sightings seemed equally far-fetched. Inevitably, some people argued that the creatures were aliens. At least that theory had the advantage of suggesting why no convincing chupacabra remains were found. Others held that the creatures were mutants created in a secret US military

laboratory on Puerto Rico – a suggestion that lost probability when similar sightings cropped up outside the island.

As the chupacabra story spread, however, and animal killings were reported from Mexico, Guatemala and other countries on the American mainland, different descriptions emerged. Alongside the hopping reptile stories, other reports spoke of hopping mammals covered in fur rather than scales. By the time the first possible dead chupacabras turned up, the accounts were rather of hairless dogs with prominent eye-sockets and a raised spinal ridge. And, indeed, scientific examination of the corpses identified them as unfamiliar types of wild dog, marked by facial deformities and mange.

Meanwhile, sceptics had begun to question the original reports on which the chupacabra legend had been built. They pointed out that it is not uncommon to find no signs of blood when animals are killed by conventional predators, partly because the heart stops pumping at the moment of death but also because insects and other opportunistic scavengers tend to clean up any gore following a kill. Although the chupacabra story remains a fascinating one, the current state of evidence suggests the animal is more likely a mythical beast than some previously undiscovered species.

163

Dragons Fire-breathing reptiles

Appearance
The classic dragon of Western tradition was a four-legged winged serpent with scaly skin and sharp claws. Chinese dragons were generally horned and bearded, with a pair of long whiskers protruding from the upper lip. Wyverns were two-legged dragons; worms, wyrms or lindworms had no legs at all.

Size
Very large. According to Pliny the Elder, Ethiopian dragons were at least 20 cubits in length, approximating to about 80ft (25m).

Lifespan
Long-lived but not immortal. In medieval legend, dragon-slaying was a staple proof of knightly valour.

Powers
Able to fly through the air and move on the ground. Many dragons breathed fire, although others killed with their venomous breath.

Habitat
Caverns, generally littered with the bones of victims. Some dragons haunted wells and pools, cutting off access for local people. Others were associated with ruined cities, palaces or castles.

Cultures across the world from the earliest times told stories of winged serpents with scaly bodies and fierce teeth and talons. Always these creatures were beings of great power, able, if they chose, to spread death and destruction in their wake. Yet in almost every other respect the accounts differed. Dragons could be good or bad, hostile or friendly, depending on who was telling the story.

Traditionally, the fundamental difference lay between East and West, for while most Western dragons were fearsome their oriental counterparts were unpredictable but often benevolent. Some Chinese dragons, such as the longwang (see pages 228–231), were associated with the sea, rivers and lakes. Others dwelled in the heavens, where it was believed that they created the clouds and made the

rain fall: "the earth coupling with the dragon" was a well-established Chinese synonym for rain.

Above all, Chinese dragons were mighty. The tianlong, or celestial dragons, guarded the home of the gods and pulled their chariots. The legendary Yellow Emperor, an early culture hero, was said to have turned into a dragon and ascended to heaven on his death, and subsequently the dragon became an imperial symbol; emperors were said to sit on the Dragon Throne and at one time it was an offence punishable by death for commoners to wear dragons embroidered on their clothes. Chinese dragon stories tended to emphasize the capricious nature of the creatures, which could serve as unassailable guardians of people who won their favour.

The devil incarnate

The Jewish tradition preserved in the Bible could hardly have been more different. Its roots apparently lay in revulsion at the primeval serpents (see pages 196–197) that featured in the most ancient Babylonian and Egyptian creation myths, which were seen by the Israelites as dangerous relics of paganism. As a result the dragon of the Book of Revelation was literally diabolic – "that

old serpent, called the Devil and Satan …" – bearing memories of the snake that first persuaded Eve to eat forbidden fruit in the Garden of Eden. Described as "a great red dragon with seven heads and ten horns and seven diadems upon his heads", the beast was slain by the Archangel Michael and thrown into a bottomless pit, only to be loosed after 1,000 years.

Saintly dragon-slayers

Michael's victory over Satan fed over the ensuing centuries into innumerable accounts of saints' triumphs over more localized and less apocalyptic beasts. The best known of the dragon-slayers was St George, historically a Roman centurion who, having refused to obey Diocletian's order to persecute Christians, was decapitated in the year 303. The first surviving reference to his struggle with a dragon postdated his death by 500 years. The story owed its enduring popularity in later times to its inclusion in *The Golden Legend*, a collection of saints' lives that became a medieval best-seller. According to its version of the story, the dragon lived in a Libyan lake and local people had to feed it a sheep and a virgin each day. Summoned to free them from their terrible tribute, St George first incapacitated the dragon with his lance,

then led the wounded beast back to the town on a leash. There he persuaded the townspeople to adopt Christianity before finally dispatching the creature with a thrust of his sword.

St George was only one of many saints credited with such feats – St Margaret, St Samson, St Clement of Metz, St Florent, St Pol and St Keyne of Cornwall were just some of the others. The stories of their exploits proved so popular that they also fed into secular legend, spawning a whole genre of tales of brave knights who, typically, returned from the Crusades to rid their home district of noxious dragons. Sometimes, as in the story of the Lambton Worm from England's

---

FAFNIR AND THE CURSED HOARD

One of world literature's most memorable dragons was Fafnir, killed by Sigurd (Siegfried in the German version) in the *Volsung Saga*, today best remembered as the basis of Wagner's *Ring* cycle of operas. Fafnir began life in human form as a son of the dwarf king Hreidmar. He conspired with his brother Regin to kill their father in order to win Andvari's cursed treasure of gold (see pages 85–86), which Hreidmar had received in reparation for the slaying of another of his sons by the god Loki. Subsequently Fafnir turned into a dragon – here a symbol of greed – to preserve the riches for himself. Regin then sent Sigurd to slay Fafnir, a feat the hero achieved by hiding in a trench so that he could stab his adversary in its soft underbelly. In the German *Nibelungenlied*, which provided Wagner's source material, Fafnir was described as a lindworm – a dragon with no legs.

County Durham, they did so by donning armour spiked with barbs like a porcupine's quills so that the dragon conveniently skewered itself while wrapping its coils around them.

Formidable guardians of treasure

An alternative strand in the dragon legends came from classical mythology. The word "dragon" derives from the Greek *drakos* ("eye"), and the dragons of Greek myth were guardians who kept watch over treasure. One such minded the golden apples in the Garden of the Hesperides, while another, killed by Thebes' founder Cadmus, kept vigil over a spring of water on the future site of the city. Famously, Cadmus then sowed the dragon's teeth, only to find that they sprang up as armed men; the warriors would have killed him if he had not thrown a precious stone among them so they fought one another. The same theme, of the dragon as treasure-keeper, also features in Norse mythology, notably in the story of Fafnir (see page 167). Oddly, it even crops up in distant China, where the fucanglong are underworld guardians of hidden riches.

Embodiments of military might

The association of dragons with warriors was easier to understand, given the creatures' reputation for strength and ferocity.

THE SALAMANDER IN THE FLAMES

In real life, salamanders are a family of amphibians related to newts. In classical and medieval legend, however, the salamander was a reptile resembling a miniature dragon that could live in fire; as such, it came to represent the element of fire itself for the ancient Greeks and their intellectual inheritors, the alchemists.

One European species is still known as the Fire salamander, even though its black-and-yellow skin is anything but fiery in colour and it cannot tolerate hot conditions. It owes its name to its habit of hibernating in damp, hollow logs. When the logs are taken for fuel and thrown on fires, the reptiles sometimes emerge from the flames, as if they had been there all the time.

In his *Memoirs*, the Renaissance goldsmith Benvenuto Cellini described one such sighting. One evening when he was about five years old, he and his family were gathered around a fire when they spotted a "little creature like a lizard … sporting in the core of the hottest coals". His father boxed his ears to make sure he remembered the sight, then kissed him and gave him some coins in recompense.

In the Middle Ages, Asian traders persuaded gullible Europeans to buy fireproof garments made of asbestos, then unknown in the West, by claiming they were made of salamander skin. The traveller Marco Polo found out the truth while en route to China, when he saw the asbestos being mined in the Tien Shan Mountains. In his account of his voyage, he was proudly able to inform his readers of the truth: the salamander was not an animal at all but rather a mineral.

The dragon was the symbol of Roman cohorts, just as the eagle was of the legions, and Norse marauders carved dragon heads on the prows of the longships that carried them on their raids. In ancient Britain the title "pendragon" (literally, dragon head) was given to some military leaders, notably Uther Pendragon, the father of King Arthur. Memories of this usage survive in the Welsh dragon, a national symbol that traces its ancestry back to the writings of Geoffrey of Monmouth in the twelfth century CE. A similar association survives in the word "dragoon", derived from a French term for infantrymen armed with carbines, which, like dragons' throats, belched forth fire.

The ubiquity of dragon legends around the world remains striking; few legendary creatures have a wider distribution. Some scholars have linked the stories with discoveries of dinosaur bones, and it may be that in early times tales of dragons served to explain away the existence of long-dead creatures of huge size. Yet no single reason can ever hope to cover all the many strands of draconian lore. More likely, gigantic winged serpents fill some archetypal need in the human imagination, crossing cultures in their power to excite awe and fear.

"The word 'dragon' derives from the Greek *drakos* ('eye'), and the dragons of Greek myth were guardians who kept watch over treasure."

Gnome Elemental spirits of the earth

Appearance
Gnarled old men with long white beards, usually dressed in clothes of primary colours and pointed caps.

Size
Small – typically only a foot or two (0.3–0.6m) high.

Lifespan
Unspecified.

Powers
The ability to move freely underground. Guardians of mineral wealth, they also came to be associated with the fertility of the soil.

Habitat
Originally the interior of the Earth. Still associated with the soil and growing plants and trees.

Few mythical beings can be credited to one man's imagination, but gnomes had a single creator: the remarkable sixteenth-century alchemist, physician and medical pioneer Theophrastus Philippus Aureolus Bombastus von Hohenheim, better known as Paracelsus.

As part of his alchemical work, Paracelsus invented the notion of elementals: spiritual beings personifying the four elements of earth, air, fire and water of which the universe was then thought to be composed. For the last two he borrowed the salamander (see page 168) and the classical water nymph Undine. The other two, though, were of his own devising: for the air the sylph, who subsequently entered popular culture as a fairy sprite, and for the earth the gnome, a name derived from the ancient Greek *gnomon*, meaning "one who knows".

THE NAIN ROUGE OF DETROIT

The city of Detroit in Michigan has legends of a harbinger of doom known as the Nain Rouge (literally, Red Dwarf), described as gnome-like in appearance: to quote one nineteenth-century source, "a shambling, red-faced creature, with a cold, glittering eye and teeth protruding from a grinning mouth".

Supposedly, the Nain Rouge appears whenever disaster strikes the city. It is said to have manifested itself before the Battle of Bloody Run in 1763, when a British attempt to relieve Fort Detroit went wrong, leaving twenty dead. It was seen in the burned-out streets of the city after the great fire of 1805, and again following General William Hull's surrender of the city to the British in the War of 1812. A woman who claimed to have been attacked by the Nain Rouge in 1884 described it as resembling "a baboon with a horned head …brilliant restless eyes and a devilish leer on its face". More recently, it was spotted on the eve of the devastating 12th Street Riot of 1967, and again in 1976 when two utility workers saw it before a fierce ice storm; it reportedly leaped 20 feet (6m) from the top of an electricity pylon and ran away.

Conceivably the Nain Rouge reflects local Native American folklore in the area. Some sources speak of Mohican tales of bearded dwarfs that worked metals and could be seen at night carousing by the light of the moon.

Paracelsus's gnomes were creatures that could move through solid earth as easily as a fish through water. Like dwarfs, they were natural guardians of mines and of buried mineral treasures. His inventions also paralleled Jewish kabbalistic traditions of beings inhabiting the interior of the Earth, and echoed the Hindu Kubera, god of wealth and guardian of subterranean treasures.

In later times gnomes became confused with other small peoples, notably the goblins and the dwarfs. They came to be portrayed as gnarled old men with long beards, typically shown wearing long, pointed hats. As such, they found a fresh incarnation in the form of garden gnomes, first produced in Germany in the mid-nineteenth century. In the spirit of Paracelsus, the original manufacturer, a Thuringian named Phillip Griebel, designed them as horticultural helpmates encouraging plants to grow. Since his time the garden gnome has become an international institution, the subject of affection and satire alike. France now has a Garden Gnome Liberation Front, devoted to returning captive gnomes to the wild, and there is even a website called Gnomes without Homes, dedicated to restoring abductees to their rightful owners.

Goblins & Orcs Malicious humanoids bent on harm

GOBLINS

Appearance
Malign humanoids with unprepossessing features. "Cat-like and rat-like/ Ratel- and wombat-like", according to Christina Rossetti.

Size
Mostly small, from 1–4ft (0.3–1.2m) in height.

Lifespan
Unspecified.

Powers
Exceptional cunning. Traditionally also ascribed shape-shifting powers and the ability to make themselves invisible.

Habitat
Some were household spirits, like kobolds. Outdoor goblins were vagrants with no settled dwellings who tended to camp out under tree roots or in mossy hollows.

Of all the little peoples that haunt the popular imagination, the goblins are the most amorphous. There is even uncertainty about their name. Some people derive it from the Greek *kobalos*, meaning a rogue. More likely, though, it came from the medieval French *gobelin*, itself allied to the German *kobold*.

Goblins, then, probably originated as the French equivalent of the household spirits known in England as boggarts (see pages 72–75). Like boggarts, they were said to prefer homes where the food and wine were plentiful and the children were pretty. They also appreciated tidiness – so much so that the easiest way to get rid of unwanted goblins was to scatter flaxseed on the floor. At first they would compulsively tidy up the mess, but after a time they would grow tired and move to a more congenial home.

Such domestic sprites were a familiar part of life in pre-industrial times, and almost every nation had its own stories of them. Yet, in English at least, the term "goblin" was imprecise enough to also be applied to certain supernatural creatures that lived outdoors. These goblins were more like earth spirits, haunting woods and lonely places and sleeping in the hollows of trees or in crevices in rocks.

In England, the outdoor goblins were regarded with affection as merry pranksters, linked to Shakespeare's Puck and the Robin Goodfellow of sixteenth- and seventeenth-century lore. They could even be industrious, like their domestic cousins. John Milton wrote in L'*Allegro* of "the drudging Goblin" who "swet/To earn his cream-bowle duly set:/When, in one night, ere glimpse of morne,/His shadowy flail hath thresh'd the corn/That ten day-labourers could not end".

From mischief to malice

More typically, though, such goblins liked to cause trouble, as catalogued in a seventeenth-century ballad describing the jests of "Robin Good-fellow, commonly called Hob Goblin". The poem described how the hobgoblin would persecute country-dwellers by sneaking up on them unseen, in his case sometimes literally so, for invisibility and shapeshifting were both within his powers. Then he might pinch or prod his victims or even imitate their voices to make rude remarks. He also liked to attend their revels as an unseen companion, helping himself to food and wine: "And to make sport,/I fart and snort,/And out the candles I doe blow;/The maides I kiss,/They shrieke, 'Who's this?',/I answer nought but 'Ho, ho, ho!'"

The hobgoblin's particular pleasure, however, was to deceive lone travellers at night. Well into the nineteenth century, people in country districts told tales of individuals heading home late, perhaps from a market or fair, who were distracted by a small figure holding up a candle or a lantern. Curious, they would follow him, maybe for several miles, over unfamiliar roads and through fields and woods. Then, even though the light still moved steadily before them, they would suddenly find themselves teetering on the brink of a rushing torrent or yawning precipice, only a step or so away from disaster. They would hear an

> "Tolkien's orcs are servile warriors with cannibalistic appetites who provide battle fodder for the evil lords of Mordor. They are, quite simply, hate-objects."

evil chuckle and the light would go out, leaving them to find their way home as best they could by their own devices.

The malice implicit in such behaviour created a reaction in the nineteenth century, when goblins turned from being supernatural tricksters into something altogether more sinister. George MacDonald's classic children's novel, *The Princess and the Goblin*, presented goblins as a subterranean people, cast in the mould of mining kobolds, fiendishly plotting to overthrow the kingdom of the eponymous princess. The merchants who peopled Christina Rossetti's extraordinary dream-poem *Goblin Market* sought to corrupt two human sisters by persuading them to eat their wares, fruits of evil that only created an insatiable craving for more.

Modern usage has tended to follow the Victorian example. Far from the roistering pranksters of Shakespeare's time, goblins today are mostly closer in spirit to their trouble-making near-namesakes, gremlins. For example, the goblins who run Gringotts Bank in the

---

THE GOD-FEARING REDCAPS

※

Redcaps were lethal goblins of northern British folklore, recognizable from their headgear, which was said to be stained with the blood of their many victims. Living in remote regions, they preyed on solitary travellers, hunting them down remorselessly in their iron boots. The only effective means of defence against these tireless pursuers was to quote the Bible, for they could not tolerate to hear the word of God.

The most notorious of all was Robin Redcap, said to haunt the ruins of Hermitage Castle, a keep deep in the border moorlands that is still one of the loneliest buildings in Britain. Robin served as a demonic imp for its infamous owner William de Soulis, a thirteenth-century marcher lord claimed by tradition to have been in league with the Devil. Legend has it that de Soulis was eventually wrapped in lead for his crimes and boiled to death in a cauldron, but Robin lived on, a malevolent presence still frequenting the scenes of his former crimes.

Harry Potter books are small, greedy and malign; few would relish having them as household companions.

Infernal inhabitants of Middle-earth

Tolkien was, then, following convention when he introduced goblins into his early work, *The Hobbit*, as villains pure and simple. A subterranean race in the spirit of *The Princess and the Goblin*, they attacked Bilbo Baggins and his companions and imprisoned them under the Misty Mountains. Yet, antiquarian scholar that he was, Tolkien was evidently not happy with the use of figures whose

pedigree of evil barely stretched back a century. So, for *The Lord of the Rings*, he devised a fresh race, the orcs, taking the word from an Anglo-Saxon term used in *Beowulf* to denote "hellish".

Filthy, vile and degraded, Tolkien's orcs are servile warriors with cannibalistic appetites who provide battle fodder for the evil lords of Mordor. They are, quite simply, hate-objects. Even at their most malicious, traditional goblins seem in comparison to be nuanced, their slyness and cunning suggesting real intelligence however vitiated by single-minded self-interest.

ORCS

Appearance
Ugly and repulsive, with deformed bodies and bow legs.

Size
Slightly smaller than humans, but powerfully built.

Lifespan
Unspecified, but mortal.

Powers
Stony-hearted, they were ferocious in battle, with a compulsion to destroy.

Habitat
Middle-earth, principally in the realm of Mordor.

175

Hybrid Beasts Manticores and other odd composites

176

Seeking to describe some unfamiliar beast that they had probably never seen with their own eyes, classical authors reached naturally for comparisons. Any tusked creature was likely to be described as boarlike; slim, horned beasts tended to be likened to goats or deer. The results as passed down through the standard sources, principally Pliny the Elder, were some very odd combinations of seemingly discrepant animal parts. Visualizing the hybrid beasts thus described strained the imagination of the artists who illustrated the medieval bestiaries.

Consider, for example, the manticore. Quoting the Greek chronicler Ctesias, Pliny described it thus: "Along with the face and ears of a man, it has a triple row of teeth that fit together like the teeth of a comb, blue-grey eyes, a lion's body the colour of blood, and it uses its tail to sting like a scorpion. Its voice falls between the sound of pan-pipes and trumpets, it is fleet-footed, and has a particular taste for human flesh."

The beast is believed to owe its name to this last trait, as "manticore" was apparently a misreading for the Greek *martichoras* or "people-eater". Pausanias,

AMEMAIT THE DEVOURER

Hybrid creatures have a long history in myth to judge from Amemait the Devourer, a figure known from ancient Egyptian wall-paintings. A monster with the head of a crocodile, the body of a lion and the hindquarters of a hippopotamus, Amemait combined elements of all the animals most feared along the Nile. The creature is known from depictions of the Egyptian equivalent of the Last Judgment, when newly dead individuals appeared before the god Osiris in the Hall of the Two Truths to swear that they had done no major wrong in their lives. As they spoke, their hearts were weighed on a scale against a feather representing truth. Those found to have been pure-hearted could look forward to an afterlife in the Fields of Aaru, the Egyptian equivalent of Heaven. Individuals who failed the test, however, were thrown to Amemait, who swallowed them up, condemning them to eternal oblivion.

writing a century later, was sceptical of some of the claims, stating: "It is said to have three rows of teeth along each jaw and spikes at the tip of its tail with which it defends itself at close quarters, while it hurls them like an archer's arrows at more distant enemies. But this is, I think, a fable that the Indians perpetuate because of their excessive fear of the beast." He suspected they were actually giving a garbled description of a lion.

Yet the manticore survived, even taking on a life of its own in later years. In early modern times there were said to be manticores in the jungles of Indonesia that could kill men merely by scratching them before gobbling them up, bones and all. T.H. White, author of *The Once and Future King*, even recorded an anecdote, possibly tongue in cheek, about an English traveller in the Andalusian region of Spain in the 1930s who was mobbed by angry villagers under the mistaken impression that he was a manticore.

Other classical hybrids might owe their origins to linguistic misunderstandings. The parandrus was described as having "the slot (hoofprint) of an ibex, branching horns, the head of a stag, the colour of a bear, and a bear's deep, shaggy coat". Its most remarkable characteristic was an ability to change colour to blend in with the surrounding vegetation,

thus avoiding detection by predators. Scholars have speculated, though, that the word was simply a false rendering of *tarandrus*, a Latin word for an unidentified northern species of deer, probably either an elk or reindeer.

Odd couples

Other creatures were created from imagined inter-species matings. The leucrota, for example, was the offspring of a hyena and a lioness. Pliny called it "the swiftest of animals", and noted that because of the stiffness of its spine it had to turn on all fours to see what was behind it. Illustrators tended to emphasize its

177

mouth, which was said to stretch from ear to ear. In place of teeth it contained two strips of bone, presumably used to grind up food for swallowing.

The yale was an antelope-like quadruped, "the size of a horse, black in colour, with an elephant's tail and the tusks of a boar". It was noted for its long, curving horns, which, remarkably, could swivel independently of one another. In combat, it would point one forward, keeping the other folded back as a spare. Modern commentators have come up with various possible derivations, ranging from the gnu to certain Kenyan cows that have one horn pointing forward and the other back; Nandi herders train them that way by binding the head with thongs. The most likely derivation, though, is the Hebrew *yael*, meaning "wild goat".

Whatever the yale's origins, it found an enduring place in heraldry. It was first adopted by John, Duke of Bedford, third son of England's King Henry IV, in the early fifteenth century. Later it became an architectural device, featuring as such, fittingly enough, above the gateway of one of the colleges of Yale University in the USA. At least one other hybrid beast, the ypotryll (see illustration, opposite), is now remembered exclusively for its heraldic usage, having the head of

JAPANESE HYBRID CREATURES

Like Western legend, Japanese folklore told stories of hybrid beasts, generally assigning them either propitious or unpropitious characteristics. The baku fell into the first category. Described as having the body of a bear, an elephant's trunk, an ox's tail and rhinoceros eyes, the baku was always a welcome guest, for it had the ability to swallow nightmares; people liked to have its image in their bedrooms as a way of sweetening their dreams.

The nue, in contrast, meant bad luck. Sporting a monkey's head on the body of a raccoon dog and with a snake for a tail, it could also manifest itself as a black cloud that hovered over ill-fated individuals, the externalized image of the depression darkening their lives. A famous tale told how a twelfth-century emperor was driven to distraction until the samurai Yorimasa Minamoto fired an arrow into the cloud that lowered over his palace each night, killing the nue within it and restoring the sovereign's peace of mind.

Another inauspicious creature was the ningyo. These merfolk (see pages 206–209) had human heads and torsos, albeit with monkey-like mouths, and fish's tails. Any fisherman who caught a ningyo knew that he was in for stormy weather, so he would throw it overboard before the bad luck could take hold.

a boar, the body of a camel, the legs of an ox and a serpent's tail.

A puzzle for theologians

Perhaps the strangest of all composite creatures was the mermecolion, said to have the foreparts of a lion and the body of a giant ant. Its origins stemmed from a simple biblical mistranslation. The only reference to the beast is in the Book of Job, where a wise man extolling God's justice remarks that "the lion perishes for want of prey". The original Hebrew text, however, used an uncommon term, *lajisch*, for "lion". Seeking to replicate the effect in Greek, the translator of the Septuagint coined the word mermecolion, apparently drawing on the term *myrmex*, used by the geographer Strabo to describe Arabian lions. But *myrmex* also happened to be the Greek for "ant".

So, in subsequent Latin translations, the ant-lion was born, and medieval scholars devoted much ingenuity to working out its theological significance. The lion, they reasoned, could only eat meat, while the ant could digest nothing but grain; small wonder, then, that the creature perished. And in just the same way, they concluded piously, a man chronically in two minds must come to nought, being inherently unstable in all his ways.

Mara Nightmare-bringers of the far North

Appearance
Wraithlike female spirits that "rode" the chests of sleepers, bringing nightmares.

Size
Maras were insubstantial, like ghosts, yet their apparent weight could cause sensations of suffocation in their victims.

Lifespan
As spirits, maras lived outside the world of time and ageing.

Powers
Caused nightmares in humans and night-sweats in horses.

Habitat
Scandinavia, where they were known at least from Norse times.

You wake up from a deep sleep, yet find yourself unable to move. The darkness presses in on you, and every breath is a mortal struggle. You feel a heavy weight pressing on your chest, harder and harder, just as if some malign force were intent on squeezing the last flutter of life out of you …

Nowadays sufferers from this condition are likely to be told that they are victims of sleep paralysis. The state occurs when the mind has woken from slumber but the body remains subject to the inhibitions on movement normal during the sleeping hours – the state that allows dreamers to think they are running without actually moving a muscle. Sleep paralysis is statistically associated with narcolepsy, but also affects a majority of ordinary, non-narcoleptic people at least once in their lives.

In earlier times people tended to personalize such conditions, blaming them not on physiology but rather on evil spirits. So they thought of the forces pressing down on the waking sleeper's chest as real, if insubstantial. For Scandinavians they took the form of wraithlike females. These were the maras, bringers of nightmares, who slipped into bedrooms at night intent on wreaking spiritual mischief.

THE SEDUCTIVE SUCCUBUS

In Western medieval Christian tradition, succubi were female demons who visited men (particularly monks) at night, giving them impure thoughts and causing wet dreams. The male equivalent of the succubus was the incubus, who similarly appeared to women. Succubi took the form of alluring temptresses. Like vampires on blood, they relied for their survival on the nocturnal emissions they elicited from their victims, who were left weakened and debilitated by the encounters. Some theologians thought that the succubi could transfer the sperm thus gained to male incubi, who then used it to impregnate human women.

There were obvious similarities between stories of the maras and the succubi. Yet the origins of the two were very different, with the Christian spirits harking back to such biblical figures as the demoness Lilith (see page 78). Then again, the maras, who were often imagined as hags, rarely had the sexual connotations that were the succubi's reason for existence.

The word *mara* meant "mare", and the spirits were thought to ride their victims like horses, sitting on their chests and so constricting their breathing. The experience was a terrifying one for those who underwent it, and this fear, combined with the maras' malicious intent, brought on nightmares.

The maras' attentions were not limited to the human occupants of the household. They could also affect domestic animals. When horses were found in their stalls in the morning restless, distressed and covered in sweat, it was assumed that maras had been riding them.

Etymological research suggests that the concept of the mara is a very ancient one; the word traces back to an Indo-European root meaning "harm". It was certainly known in Norse times, for it appears in the *Ynglinga Saga*, written down by Snorri Sturluson in the thirteenth century CE. From Scandinavia it radiated outward, changing slightly on the way. The Polish equivalent of the mara was the *nocnitsa* or night-hag, who might come to trouble children's sleep unless deterred by the presence of iron in the bed or cradle. Elsewhere in the Slav world, people told tales of the kikimora, a nightmare spirit said to be the soul of a girl who had died unbaptized. The kikimora might take the form of a moth

or a wisp of hair, settling on a sleeper's lips to cause symptoms similar to those brought on by the mara. Victims would sometimes fill the keyholes of their bedroom doors with beeswax, hoping thereby to keep out the evil spirit.

Today the most familiar representation of a mara is probably Henry Fuseli's famous picture of *The Nightmare* (see above), painted in 1782. The work shows a grotesque imp squatting on the chest of a sleeping woman while a panicked horse stares blindly through the drapes behind her bed. The image has become an icon of the Romantic era, capturing the sense of mingled horror and helplessness that maras themselves inspired, and embodying as they did all the terrors of the evil dreams they brought.

Trolls & Ogres   Malign giants with murder in mind

Appearance
Mostly big, squat and ugly, although in one tradition female trolls could be comely and attractive to men.

Size
From large to immense.

Lifespan
Longer than human.

Powers
Great strength, coupled in some cases with the ability to shift shape and make themselves invisible. Ogres were cannibalistic.

Habitat
Trolls lived in Scandinavia. Ogres were found around the world.

Trolls were the best-known beings of Scandinavian folklore, but they were also among the most confusing. The word itself could apply to almost any dangerous supernatural creature with magical powers. Over time, different traditions evolved, so that the trolls of Denmark and Sweden ended up very different from those of Norway and Iceland.

In the manner of the Irish fairy folk, Danish trolls formed an alternative society living in uneasy proximity to

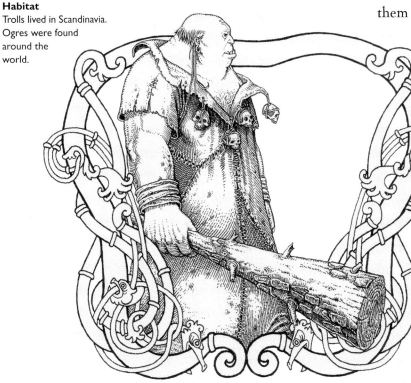

the human world. Like fairies they had homes underground, under mounds or hills, where they were thought to hoard treasure just as leprechauns did. Strangers might meet one of the trolls by the wayside and mistake him or her for a fellow-human; the womenfolk in particular were often good-looking, although there were giveaway signs – most typically a tail poking out underneath a dress, as with Japanese kitsune. Sometimes their sheer elegance gave them away, making them look out of place in the forest.

Individuals who encountered a troll were well advised to take evasive action, for their kind generally wished humans no good. They could make themselves invisible and sneak into people's homes to steal food and drink or hold destructive parties. Worse, they took newborn babies, again like fairies, leaving changelings in their place. The easiest way to get rid of them was to show some Christian symbol, such as a Bible or a cross, for they were irredeemably pagan. Famously, they could not stand the sound of church bells.

The Norwegian trolls were very different. For a start, they were solitary. They were also spectacularly ugly: hairy, with big noses and long arms, and sometimes also tusks or a single eye. They lived in gloomy castles, often set on mountaintops, or else in an icy realm in the far North known as Trollebotten. They could only go out at night, for exposure to sunlight could turn them to stone – many rock features in the Norwegian and Icelandic landscapes were said to represent the petrified visages of trolls.

Above all, these trolls were big: they were natural descendants of the giants of Norse myth, and like them were said to be enemies of the storm god Thor. Even now people sometimes claim that thunderbolts kill trolls.

Victims of their own stupidity

In their size and aggression the Norwegian trolls had much in common with ogres. These malevolent giants were the brain-child of storytellers, and their popularity spread through fairy-tales. The word itself is thought to have been coined by the seventeenth-century French author Charles Perrault, who

---

HEROES AND ANTI-HEROES

If ogres were conscious fictional creations from the start, it is hardly surprising that modern tale-tellers have chosen to play tricks with their image. The French author Michel Tournier gave the protagonist of his Goncourt Prize-winning *Le Roi des Aulnes* (translated as *The Ogre*) a paedophile dimension. Set in Second World War France and Germany, the novel traces the extraordinary exploits of Abel Tiffauges, a childlike innocent with a very peculiar, although asexual, fascination for pre-pubescent boys. Wrongly accused of child molesting, then taken prisoner of war, he ends up being enlisted by his Nazi captors to kidnap boys and deliver them to an élite training camp.

In a very different spirit the creators of *Shrek*, by a neat piece of role reversal, made an ogre the eponymous hero of their animation hit – and, with a fine sense of restorative justice, even let him win the heart of an independent-minded princess.

---

introduced Cinderella, Sleeping Beauty and Puss in Boots to the world.

Like Tolkien's orcs, ogres were designed from the start to be detestable. Big, clumsy and aggressive, they exuded a dull malevolence in all their actions, from terrorizing villages to abducting princesses. Worse still, they were cannibals, with a particular fondness for gobbling up young children – a detail guaranteed to make impressionable young listeners wriggle nervously in their beds at nights. Yet they were also slow-witted, which meant that they were regularly outsmarted, bringing some much-needed comfort before the bedtime stories came to an end.

Apemen Hairy humanoids of the world's wild places

Appearance
Most accounts speak of human-like figures standing on two legs but covered in reddish-brown or dark fur over all the body, usually excepting the face, the palms of the hands and the soles of the feet.

Size
Reports vary. Accounts of sasquatches claim large males can be 8ft or more (2.5m) tall. The Mongolian almas is said to be of average human height, while the Indonesian *orang pendek* is smaller, ranging from 2ft, 6in to 5ft (0.8–1.5m).

Lifespan
Unknown.

Powers
Great strength, and the sturdiness needed to survive in the wild.

Habitat
Remote regions of many parts of the world, with the bulk of reported sightings coming from East Asia and the west coast of North America.

Reports of fur-covered creatures standing on two legs and variously described as apelike or humanoid are among the most persistent and widespread in all the records of cryptozoology – the study of species purported to exist but not yet known to science. Such accounts have come from every continent except Antarctica, but with a particular preponderance from East Asia and the west coast of North America.

In America the beings tend to be known as sasquatches on the Canadian side of the border but in the USA in the generic singular as Bigfoot. Their habitat lies in the great woods of the Rocky Mountain foothills, where there have been several dozen reported sightings over the past century and at least one purported filming. Reports of sasquatches generally emphasize their size – they are typically said to be between 6 and 8 feet (1.8–2.5m) in height – and are otherwise mostly consistent in speaking of a pelt of dark brown or reddish hair covering the entire body.

The most spectacular of the first-person encounters was that of Albert Ostman, a retired logger who in 1957 told an investigator that he had been held captive by an entire family of sasquatches while on a camping trip near Toba Inlet in British Columbia thirty-three years earlier. He claimed to have stayed with the creatures for six days, during which time they treated him with curiosity but did not harm him. He eventually escaped by giving the dominant male a can of snuff, running away while the sasquatch was incapacitated after swallowing the contents whole. Supposedly, Ostman kept silent about his adventure at the time because he feared being disbelieved. Inevitably, sceptics have suggested the whole story was a trick of memory, based on something he once dreamed or merely imagined.

Bigfoot on the big screen

The supposed apeman footage was taken in October 1967 by two Bigfoot hunters, a one-time rodeo rider named Roger Paterson and his friend Bob Gimlin, in the wooded highlands of northern California, near the Oregon border. Barely a minute long, it shows a large

female with pendulous breasts, reckoned by Paterson to have been at least 6 feet 6 inches (2m) tall, seen across a clearing from a distance of about 40 yards (36.5m). The creature, resembling a large, bipedal ape, briefly looks toward the camera before striding away into the woods. The film has been subjected to endless, inconclusive analysis. Sceptics suspect an elaborately staged hoax featuring a human in a specially designed gorilla suit; believers point to unusual anatomical details and to peculiarities in the creature's stride to insist that the film was genuine.

At the time that the film was taken, it inevitably roused memories of the Himalayan yeti, which had been much in the news over the previous fifteen years. Previously known through a mistranslation as the "Abominable Snowman", the yeti in fact takes its name from a Tibetan word meaning "rock-bear". Again, there was a long local tradition of sightings, and at least one Buddhist monastery had preserved a supposed yeti scalp that on scientific investigation in fact turned out probably to have come from some hoofed animal, perhaps a serow (a type of mountain goat).

"A fascinating fairy-tale"?

What brought the yeti to prominence was a rash of sightings by Western mountaineers in the 1950s and '60s. Even Sir Edmund Hillary and Tenzing Norgay, the conquerors of Everest, reported seeing giant footprints on their epic climb of 1953. Hillary was sufficiently intrigued to include yeti-hunting among the goals of a scientific expedition to the Himalayan region

that he led seven years later. The results, however, were disappointing, and the explorer came away convinced that tales of the snowmen were no more than "a fascinating fairy-tale" nurtured by superstition and distant glimpses of existing known animals.

Further sightings have been reported, but no definite evidence of the creature's existence has emerged. Recently, several investigators have concluded that some of the sightings might have actually been of the endangered Himalayan brown bear, which can walk on its hind legs.

Yet the legends of apemen refuse to die. From China come tales of the *yeren* or wild man said to inhabit remote forest regions of the south and west (see box, below). Malaysian legend speaks

---

THE WILDMAN OF DEEPEST CHINA

Tales of hirsute hominids have been emerging from China for centuries past, and in recent times have stimulated some scientific interest. In 1961 a team was sent to investigate a report that road-builders had killed a female creature in the province of Yunnan. No body was found, however, and the researchers concluded that the animal involved was probably a gibbon. Similarly, two preserved, human-like hands subjected to tests in 1980 were eventually reckoned to come from a large macaque, although possibly of a previously unknown subspecies. Even so, stories of the *yeren* or "wildman" continue to circulate, causing speculation that a relict population of *Gigantopithecus* – an apelike creature known to have inhabited southern China in the Pleistocene era, ending 10,000 years ago – might somehow have survived in remote forest areas. Investigators have been intrigued by the similarity between some eyewitness accounts of long-armed beings as much as 7 feet (over 2m) tall and North American accounts of encounters with sasquatches.

of the *orang mawas*, a gigantic hominid from the Johor jungle region that was the object of a government-backed expedition early in 2006. In Indonesia the *orang pendek* (literally "short person") is a much smaller creature that has been reported many times, particularly in the forests of Sumatra.

In time firm evidence may emerge for the existence of at least one of these creatures, and the world will celebrate the discovery of a new primate that walks on two legs. For now, though, the apemen remain conjectural, still hesitantly confined to the domain of myth rather than of hard science.

THE ALMAS — PRE-HUMAN SURVIVOR OR MYTHIC INVENTION?

Early in the fifteenth century, a Bavarian nobleman named Hans Schiltberger was captured by the Turks and handed over to a Mongolian prince called Egidi. The prisoner was taken to an area thought to have been in the Altai mountains of western Mongolia. Writing later of his captivity, he noted: "Wild people who have nothing in common with other humans live in the mountains. Fur covers their entire body except for the face and hands. They run around in the hills like animals and eat foliage and grass and whatever else they can find." He then went on to speak of wild horses in the region — presumably the indigenous species called Przewalski's horse, which has only been known to science since the 1870s.

Schiltberger's account is taken to be one of the earliest surviving descriptions of the Almas, a race of wild humans said to inhabit mountainous regions of Central Asia and Mongolia. Oral tradition long treated them as part of the local fauna, with no supernatural or mythical connotations, and they were mostly regarded without fear. They were described as between 5 and 6 feet (1.5–1.8m) tall, with bodies covered in reddish-brown hair, and they generally went about naked. They had prominent brow-ridges on their faces, along with flat noses and receding chins. Such descriptions have led some researchers to speculate that they may have represented a relict Neanderthal population.

A wild woman, thought locally to have been an Almas, was captured in the late nineteenth century and lived out her life on a farm in the Caucasus. Zana, as she was known, at first reacted violently to her capture but eventually calmed down enough to be allowed to move freely around the farm, where she carried out simple chores. She also had several children, fathered by a local man, who were said to be swarthy in appearance and unusually strong, but otherwise entirely integrated into the human community. Recently, a scientific study of a skull said to be that of one of her sons reported no evident Neanderthal traits, suggesting that Zana too had probably belonged to *Homo sapiens sapiens*, the modern human species.

Squonk Doleful denizen of the American backwoods

188

Appearance
Hideously ugly, with ill-fitting, warty skin.

Size
Around 3ft (1m) tall.

Lifespan
Unrecorded.

Powers
Limited. Squonks themselves felt they had little to boast of.

Habitat
The backwoods of Pennsylvania in northeastern USA.

Logging was always hard work for the men who gave their lives to it, but life in the big forests created a compensating sense of camaraderie among the woodsmen. The work was seasonal, and while there was timber to be felled, the lumberjacks often left their homes to live in tents or communal bunkhouses. There they whiled away the evenings chatting and telling stories. They particularly liked yarns that were comical and far-fetched, serving both to entertain and alarm newcomers to their enclosed and isolated world.

Around 1910 a certain William Thomas Cox from Minnesota started collecting some of the taller tales, as told by loggers across the USA and into Canada. He recounted them in a short collection, just forty-eight pages long, that he entitled *Fearsome Creatures of the Lumberwoods, with a few Desert and Mountain Beasts*. Long considered lost, the book has since been rediscovered and is now freely available on the Internet. Its re-emergence marks a quirky addition to the annals of mythical beasts, even if

in this case the myths were never meant to be taken too seriously.

The fearsome critters that Cox described include one or two familiar names, notably the leprechaun (see pages 90–92). Most, though, were true originals. There was the hugag, a moose-like creature whose unjointed legs prevented it from ever lying down; the apelike agropelter, whose delight was to throw rotten treelimbs at passing lumbermen; and the whirling whimpus, a gorilla-like predator that haunted forest tracks where it span so fast on its feet as to make itself invisible to its prey. Any creatures unlucky enough to walk into it "became instantly deposited in the form of syrup or varnish on the huge paws of the whimpus".

A martyr to its own ugliness

Yet the star of Cox's collection was undoubtedly the squonk. As he described it, this melancholic creature was a martyr to its own ugliness. Misshapen and with ill-fitting skin covered in warts and other blemishes, it suffered from permanently low self-esteem. In its home – it occupied a restricted habitat in the hemlock forests of northern Pennsylvania – it did little but hide itself away and cry. It rarely moved from its lair except at twilight, fearing to be seen abroad. Any contact with the outside world was enough to reduce it to paroxysms of tears.

The tracks of its tears

The squonk's lachrimosity was no doubt increased by the fact that, like other forest animals, it was sometimes hunted. Stalkers followed the trail of its tears over the forest floor and listened for the sounds of weeping. Cox related that a hunter named J.P. Wentling once succeeded in tracking one down and coaxed it into a bag by mimicking its doleful cry. Yet his ingenuity did him little good. As he carried his prize back through the woods, he heard sounds of liquid lamentation, and when he looked in the sack it was to find his prey had dissolved entirely, leaving behind only a damp patch and a few bubbles.

In 1967 the Argentinian man of letters Jorge Luis Borges included the squonk in his *Book of Imaginary Beings*, introducing the creature to a wider world. It subsequently even found its way into rock music via a song of

the same name on the 1976 Genesis album A *Trick of the Tail*. For, like all the best mythical creatures, the squonk touched a sympathetic chord in the human imagination and even pointed a moral: about the destructive force of self-pity, which can reduce people and beasts alike to nought – or, in its case, to a small puddle.

Spider Beasts Demon spirits or trickster heroes?

Appearance
Anansi usually appeared in human form, as did most Japanese spider demons until their true nature was revealed.

Size
Variable. Japanese spider demons were often described as gigantic.

Lifespan
Unspecified.

Powers
Anansi was credited with unusual cunning. Evil spider spirits were typically hunters that sucked their victims dry.

Habitat
Tales of Anansi came from many parts of West Africa, and subsequently from the Caribbean and the American mainland. Spider demons were a feature of Japanese myth.

Spiders owe their scientific name of arachnids to the Greek myth of Arachne, who rashly challenged the goddess Athene to a weaving contest. Athene's tapestry portrayed her own greatness, while Arachne chose to depict the amorous conquests of Zeus. Outraged at the mortal woman's temerity, Athene struck down Arachne's work and destroyed her loom. Arachne fled in shame and hanged herself. Taking pity on her fate, Athene turned the rope from which she was suspended into a web and made Arachne herself a spider, always busy weaving.

The world of myth has always taken a contradictory view of spiders, sometimes reviling them but more often treating them as beneficial creatures. Folk tales in the Christian and Islamic traditions recounted how on the one hand the infant Jesus and on the other the prophet Muhammad were saved from pursuers by spiders that spun webs over the openings of caves where they were sheltering. A famous story from Scottish history had the hero-king Robert the Bruce finding the will to successfully challenge for the Scottish throne after watching a spider fail six times to build a web on the roof of the cavern where he was hiding, only to succeed at the seventh attempt.

Perhaps it was not surprising, then, that the most celebrated spider-creature of myth should be a hero – the trickster Anansi. The subject of a whole cycle of stories in his native West Africa, Anansi started life as a creator god, responsible for putting the Sun and Moon in the sky. Stories of his doings travelled to the New World in the slave ships, and there he found a new lease of life as a cunning wheeler-dealer, famed for his resourcefulness. In most of the stories Anansi functioned as an ordinary human,

---

THE LAIR OF SHELOB

One of Frodo Baggins's most terrifying encounters in *The Lord of the Rings* is with Shelob, a giant female arachnid living high in the mountains of Mordor. While travelling through the mountains, Baggins disturbs Shelob, whereupon she paralyzes the hero with a lethal sting. He is rescued only after his loyal assistant Sam Gamgee succeeds in wounding her and forcing her to retreat to her lair. J.R.R. Tolkien created the monster for the book, drawing her name from the word "lob", an archaic term for "spider".

although he sometimes escaped danger by reverting to spider form.

The benevolent view of spiders still lingers in story today, as the popularity of E.B. White's children's classic *Charlotte's Web* suggests. Yet it has mostly been replaced by a negative attitude, summed up by the success of films such as *Tarantula* or *Arachnophobia* that present spiders as objects of horror.

This tradition too has a long pedigree, particularly in Japan. In one tale, a warrior named Yorimitsu was sent out by his emperor to rid the land of demons.

He fell ill and was tended by a boy who brought him a cup of medicine each day, but this only made him feel worse. Losing patience, Yorimitsu threw the beaker at the boy's head, only to find himself instantly caught in a sticky web.

Arriving at this critical moment, the hero's faithful companion stabbed Yorimitsu's tormentor, who took to his heels and fled. A trail of blood led the two pursuers to a huge spider, bleeding from a sword thrust. They quickly finished off the demon, whereupon Yorimitsu's health was restored.

191

Apocalyptic Beasts Fauna of the biblical end-time

Appearance
Varied. Including locusts with human faces that looked like horses arrayed for battle; horses with the heads of lions and serpents for tails; a seven-headed red dragon representing Satan; a beast from the sea resembling a leopard but with a bear's feet and a lion's mouth ... .

Size
Unspecified, but in some cases cosmic: the red dragon used its tail to sweep a third of the stars from the sky.

Lifespan
After a first defeat by the forces of the Lord, the red dragon is destined to be thrown into a bottomless pit for 1,000 years. He will then be loosed to lead the forces of evil in a final battle, after which he will be consigned forever to a lake of fire.

Powers
The ability to destroy the godless through war and pestilence and to challenge, although not to defeat, the forces of the Lord.

Habitat
Revealed by Christ in a vision to John of Patmos, who saw into Heaven as though through an open door.

192

The Book of Revelation, the last in the Christian Bible, is a relatively short text, but it has generated more controversy than almost any other work of comparable size. It describes two visions accorded to its author, who gives his name as John, while in exile on the Greek island of Patmos. The first takes the form of instructions, delivered by Christ himself through John, to seven specified Christian communities on the mainland of what is now Turkey. This section is relatively short, occupying just three of the book's twenty-two chapters.

The last nineteen chapters describe a single vision, again revealed by Christ, who summons John to Heaven to see the glory of the Lord. Jesus then unfastens the seven seals securing a scroll held in God's right hand that contains the secrets of the end of the world. With the opening of each of the first six seals, a visionary sight appears, the first four being the celebrated Four Horsemen of the Apocalypse (see page 195).

The opening of the seventh seal sets in motion a new phase of the vision. Seven angels successively appear and blow their trumpets, unleashing a series of disasters on the Earth. The seventh angel heralds a complex sequence of images, seemingly representing in symbolic form the situation in which the persecuted Christian community found itself in John's day. The final part of the work describes the events leading up to the Last Judgment and the emergence of a new, heavenly Jerusalem in which God will rule over the saved.

"Four living creatures full of eyes"

Symbolic beasts feature at several different points in the story. When John has his first sight of God in glory, he sees "four living creatures full of eyes" surrounding his throne. Between them, the quartet symbolize the greater part of God's creation: one is like a lion, representing the carnivores, another an ox for the herbivores. The third has the face of a man, indicating the human presence, while the fourth, an eagle, stands for the birds of the air. The eyes apparently indicate perpetual watchfulness.

Other creatures are less benevolent. When the fifth angel blows his trumpet,

he unleashes a plague of locusts upon unbelievers – "those of mankind who do not have the seal of God upon their foreheads". These heavenly locusts are unlike any seen before, for they appear "like horses arrayed for battle". They have human faces with women's hair but bear the tails of scorpions, equipped with venomous stings. Once they have completed their ravages, the sixth angel's trumpet introduces fresh horrors in the form of a flood of armed horsemen riding on mounts that have heads like lions, breathing smoke and sulphur, and serpents for tails.

Visions of the seventh angel

The most memorable of the beasts, however, come in the section following the sounding of the seventh angel's trumpet. This episode begins with the vision of a female figure, the Woman Clothed with the Sun, who bears a child, "one who is to rule all nations with a rod of iron". A red dragon with seven heads and ten horns then appears, identified in the text as "that ancient serpent, who is called the Devil and Satan". The dragon pursues the woman, who would seem to be a symbol of the Lord's elect or the Christian Church. While her child – evidently Jesus – is taken up into the safety of Heaven, the woman herself flees into the wilderness in search of refuge. In similar fashion the Christian community itself was scattered and dispersed in John's day.

Two other symbolic beasts thereupon make their appearance. One, also with seven heads and ten horns, emerges from the sea. It is described as resembling a leopard with a bear's feet and a lion's mouth. The dragon gives it power on Earth and people worship it, saying "Who is like the beast, and who can fight against it?" The second, rising from the Earth, "had two horns like a lamb and it spoke like a dragon". This one is said to exercise all the authority of the first beast and to make the Earth and its inhabitants worship it.

The number of the beast

This latter creature causes its own name – the infamous "mark of the beast" – to be inscribed on the right hand or

"'This call for wisdom,' John states, 'let him who has understanding reckon the number of the beast, for it is a human number, its number is 666.'"

194

forehead of anyone wanting to conduct business within its realm. This mark is specifically contrasted with the seal of righteousness borne on the temples of the 144,000 followers of the Lamb (Jesus Christ) proclaiming the name of the Lord. The mark is said to bear the name of the beast, or rather a number representing that name. John gives a very specific clue to its identity. "This call for wisdom," he states, "let him who has understanding reckon the number of the beast, for it is a human number, its number is 666."

Deciphering the code

Arabic numerals of the type we use today were not in use at the time John was writing. Instead, numbers were represented by letters; the Roman "C", for example, stood for 100. As a result, numerical codes were common, and John evidently had recourse to one in this instance. Over the centuries scholars have devoted much ingenuity to working his message out, and today something like a consensus has finally emerged over its interpretation. Linguists have pointed out that if the phrase *Neron Kaisar* – the normal way of writing "Emperor Nero" in Greek at the time – is transcribed into John's native Hebrew, the numerical value of the

---

THE FOUR HORSEMEN OF THE APOCALYPSE

In the course of his vision, John watches the Lamb (representing Christ) opening the seven seals of a scroll, held in God's right hand, that reveals the secret of the world's predestined end. As each of the first four seals is opened, a horseman appears.

The first rides a white horse, carries a bow, and is given a crown; he is taken to symbolize Conquest. The second, mounted on a red horse, receives a great sword, the image of War. The third, whose mount is black, bears a balance in his hand and stands for Pestilence. The fourth, on a pale horse, is Death. Taken together, the four horsemen are symbolic forces of destruction on a massive scale, loosed by the Lord to wreak havoc on the godless.

---

characters employed adds up to exactly six hundred and sixty-six.

With this identification in mind, the symbolism of the beasts falls into place. The Beast of the Earth is Nero himself, a notorious persecutor of Christians. In his day all Rome's subjects were expected to worship the emperors as gods in pagan ceremonies. So, for John, attending the rituals stamped people with the mark of the beast, just as celebrating Christian rites identified the saved. The Beast of the Sea, then, was the Roman Empire itself, worshipped by extension through the reverences paid to its rulers. And both, in John's view, were servants of the red dragon, Satan himself, the eternal persecutor of all that is just and holy.

Monstrous Serpents Primeval powerhouses

Appearance
Snakelike, sometimes with more than one head.

Size
From the cosmic – the Earth and sky were made from the body of the Babylonian Tiamat – to relatively small. The tsuchinoko, a legendary Japanese snake creature whose middle is fatter than its head or tail, is less than 3ft (1m) long.

Lifespan
Unspecified, but rarely immortal. Many serpent myths describe the creatures' death at the hands of gods or heroes.

Powers
In some cases, almost limitless powers of destruction. The Egyptian Apep struggled with Ra nightly, threatening to unleash chaos on the world.

Habitat
Worldwide wherever snakes are found, with a particular preponderance in the lands in and around the Fertile Crescent, from Egypt and Greece to Iran.

According to the Babylonian creation epic the *Enuma Elish*, dating back deep into the second millennium BCE, the world as we know it was the result of a cosmic struggle. The two contenders were Marduk, king of the gods, and Tiamat, the primeval serpent goddess of the sea who had been their original progenitor. Marduk trapped his adversary in a net; when she opened her mouth to swallow him he called upon the winds to hold it ajar long enough for him to shoot an arrow into her gullet. Having killed her, he then split her body in two, using the upper half to form the heavens and the lower portion for the Earth.

Tiamat was the first in a line of primordial serpents that crowd the pages of myth. Sometimes the creatures were difficult to distinguish from dragons, with which they had much in common, including a history of destruction at the hands of heroes, human or divine. The imagery obviously drew on people's innate fear of venomous snakes, a real threat in many of the lands where the legends developed. The stories also probably fed on one another, so that distant memories of Tiamat came to underlie the myths of several neighbouring lands.

One such may have been ancient Egypt, where tales of a cosmic serpent named Apep (now known in more familiar Greek form as Apophis) spread from Middle Kingdom times. Like Tiamat, Apep (shown opposite) was a symbol of destruction and primeval chaos, the sworn enemy of the sun god Ra. Each evening Apep lurked just below the horizon to ambush Ra as he sailed past on his solar boat, attempting to block the river leading into the Underworld with his gigantic coils. And almost every evening Ra succeeded in evading his clutches, thanks to the efforts of a band of divine allies who helped him fight off the serpent. However often they won, Ra's reprieve was always only temporary for, as a creature of the Underworld, Apep could not be killed.

Forces of creation and destruction

Other mythologies also had stories of superhuman serpents, from the Greek Echidna – half-woman, half-snake and mother of monsters – to the Aztec

Xiuhcoatl, the fire-serpent personification of drought. Yet in some traditions snake-gods had a more positive image. The best-known example was probably Aido Hwedo, venerated by the Fon of Dahomey in west Africa. Aido Hwedo was the principal assistant of the creator goddess Mawu, who travelled in his mouth on her journey to make the world. Aido Hwedo also did some creating of his own, for mountains were formed from his piled excrement. Once the Earth was formed, he coiled himself up beneath it to bear its weight, and there he still lies, causing earthquakes when he stirs. The sea was set around the Earth to keep him cool.

The Fon even had an end-time legend that chimes neatly with modern ecological worries about the exhaustion of natural mineral resources. Aido Hwedo lives on the iron in the earth, they maintained, and when he has finally used up all the reserves, he will be reduced by hunger to eating himself, tail first. Then the Earth itself will collapse, and the creation he helped establish will come to an end.

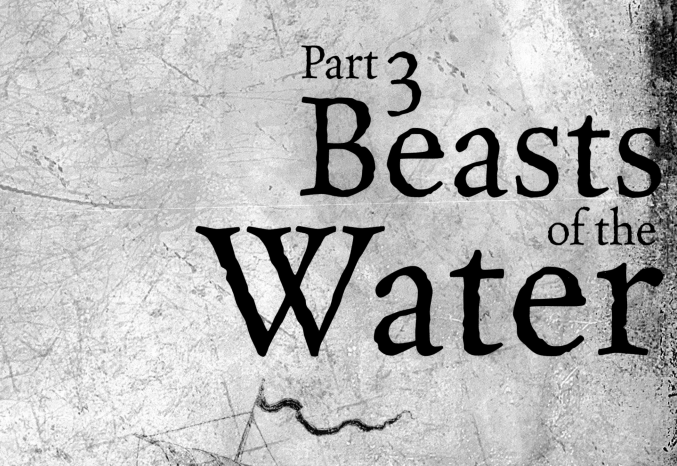

Part 3
Beasts
of the
Water

Leviathan The dragon that is in the sea

Appearance
"The dragon that is in the sea", breathing out fire and smoke. "His breath kindles coals, and a flame comes forth from his mouth."

Size
Massive. "He makes the deep boil like a pot."

Lifespan
According to the Old Testament Book of Isaiah, Leviathan will be killed by the Lord in the endtime. Yet Psalms 74:14 suggests God already "crushed the heads of Leviathan" at the time of the creation, "giving him as food for the creatures of the wilderness".

Powers
Fearless, formidable and unvanquished – none but God can tame Leviathan. "When he raises himself up, the mighty are afraid. … The sword cannot avail against him, nor the spear, the dart or the javelin."

Habitat
"The sea great and wide … where go the ships, and Leviathan which Thou didst form to sport in it." (Psalm 104)

Leviathan is the primeval sea monster of the Old Testament, which the Lord, according to the prophet Isaiah, will punish in the final day of reckoning. The monster is also mentioned in the Book of Job and in the Psalms, and the different references seem to reflect separate traditions of its origins.

Easily the most detailed description comes in the Book of Job, where the Lord taunts Job with humankind's inability to capture or tame either Leviathan or its land equivalent, the hippopotamus-like Behemoth (see pages 56–57). A whole chapter enumerates the beast's fearsome attributes. Job's Leviathan has a double coat of mail, a back "made of rows of shields", and underparts that "are like sharp potsherds". Dragon-like, the creature breathes out flames – "out of his mouth go flaming torches; sparks of fire leap forth" – and leaves a shining wake as it moves across the ocean.

Various attempts have been made to identify Leviathan with specific creatures. Some authorities have seen a link with the Nile crocodile in the beast's scales, joined so closely together

"that no air can come between them". Some such connection would neatly parallel the identification of Behemoth with the African hippopotamus. Others have chosen to concentrate on Leviathan's size and see an association with the whale, citing Psalm 104's reference to the various creatures that inhabit the ocean, the greatest of which is "Leviathan, which Thou didst form to sport in it". Modern Hebrew makes the connection evident, using the word simply to mean "whale".

Neither comparison, however, sits well with Isaiah's description of "the dragon that is in the sea" or with the fire-breather described in the Book of Job. Those references suggest an entirely different source – in myth.

Leviathan and Tiamat
The Canaanites, Israel's neighbours in the Promised Land, told stories of an epic battle between their god Baal and a seven-headed sea monster named Lotan – equivalent to "Leviathan" in the Ugaritic language. This legend in turn was only one of several accounts of struggles with

"Dragon-like, the creature breathes out flames – 'out of his mouth go flaming torches; sparks of fire leap forth' – and leaves a shining wake as it moves across the ocean."

primeval sea monsters, the best known probably being that told in the *Enuma Elish*. This poem describing the creation of the world came from Mesopotamia, on the other horn of the Fertile Crescent. Its hero, the god Marduk, confronted his own mother Tiamat, the monstrous goddess of salt water and also of primordial chaos. The contest was a terrible one, not least because Tiamat raised up a company of horrifying creatures to aid her: "the Worm, the Dragon, the She-monster, the Great Lion, the Mad Dog, the Scorpion Man, the Howling Storm, Kulili and Kusariqu". But the resourceful Marduk prepared a net and rode on the storm, "his terrible chariot", to meet her. Entangling her in the net's meshes, he then shot her dead with an arrow from his bow. Subsequently, he split her body apart "like a cockle-shell", using the two halves to create Earth and sky.

Memories of the story survived in Israel, to judge from a reference in the apocryphal Book of Enoch. It identified the two parts of the body respectively with Leviathan and Behemoth, claiming: "And on that day the two monsters will be parted: one, the she-monster Leviathan, to dwell in the abyss of the ocean over the fountains of water, and the other, the male beast named Behemoth, which dwells in an invisible desert whose name is Dundayin, east of the Garden of Eden."

The Isaiah reference similarly cast the fate of Leviathan in the future, although in rather different terms. It appears in a section of the book sometimes known as the "Isaiah apocalypse", forecasting a coming time of destruction when the Lord will vent his wrath upon a sinning Earth. Besides foreseeing widespread desolation and depopulation, the work also predicts that "In that day the Lord with his hard and great and strong sword will punish Leviathan the fleeing serpent, Leviathan the twisting serpent, and he will slay the dragon that is in the sea".

The battle with Behemoth

Later traditions elaborated on similar themes. Jewish lore spoke of a mighty battle between Leviathan and Behemoth that would take place at the End of Days, when the primordial beasts of the sea and of the land would finally slay one another, or be slain by the Lord. A further variation had Jehovah displaying his power by killing Leviathan and feeding her flesh to the righteous in a tent made from her own skin. This Talmudic Leviathan is also female, perhaps in lingering memory of Tiamat.

Christian sources in the Middle Ages favoured a male Leviathan, taking their inspiration from the last phrase of the Book of Job's description, which calls the creature "king over all the sons of pride". On this authority, Leviathan was identified with the Devil, and Hell was sometimes represented as lying within the monster's gaping maw.

The seventeenth-century English political theorist Thomas Hobbes, quoted the same passage in its entirety to explain his reasons for entitling his greatest work *Leviathan*: "There is nothing on Earth to be compared with him. He is made so as not to be afraid. He sees every high thing below him; and is king over all the sons of pride." For Hobbes, the description made the beast a fitting symbol for the authority of the state and, by extension, for the ruler who personified it.

Yet for the most part such interpretations remained peripheral. In normal usage Leviathan remained the primordial creature of the depths, and so it is to this day, a metaphor for anything vast and awesome that lies hidden under the ocean's surface.

JORMUNGAND THE WORLD SERPENT

Norse myth also had tales of a primeval sea creature, the formidable Jormungand. He was born as one of three monstrous offspring of the malign god Loki and the giantess Angrboda, his siblings being the wolf Fenrir and Hel, icy queen of the Underworld. Fearing the evil that the trio might wreak, the god Odin threw Jormungand into the sea. There he grew and grew until he was large enough to encircle the world. He lay on the seabed meditating revenge against the gods, and his occasional writhings stirred up tempests.

Jormungand was the particular enemy of Thor, for the two were predestined to meet in mortal combat at Ragnarok. In that day of doom, the world serpent will make his way to shore, causing the oceans to flood the land. Once on land, Jormungand's poisonous breath will blight the soil and the sky. He will confront Thor, who will eventually kill him – but only after the serpent's venom has entered the god's bloodstream, so that he too will collapse and die just nine paces away from the creature's body.

Scylla & Charybdis A helmsman's dilemma

SCYLLA

Appearance
Multi-headed sea monster with 3 rows of teeth in each head. Beneath a woman's torso she had a dog's body with 12 legs.

Size
Supernaturally large. The necks of her 6 heads were long enough to pluck seamen off passing ships.

Lifespan
Magically cursed to live beyond mortal span.

Powers
Snatched sailors avoiding the whirlpool Charybdis with any one of her 6 mouths.

Habitat
A cave on the Italian shore of the Strait of Messina, separating Italy and Sicily.

The narrows separating Sicily from the Italian mainland have long been considered dangerous waters. Even today, small whirlpools caused by counter-currents appear and disappear, and louring, anfractuous rocks threaten shipwreck for any navigator careless enough to steer too close to them. In ancient times, when boats were powered by sail or oar, they were much more of a challenge, and veteran seafarers heading through the strait told a story to terrify novices with the dangers of the passage.

Theirs was a strange tale of two beautiful girls turned by divine wrath into monsters. Scylla was a sea nymph, so beautiful that she attracted the attention of the sea god Poseidon himself. Amphitrite, Poseidon's wife, saw her husband's infatuation and determined

to be revenged. So she went to the fountain where Scylla bathed and poured in a noxious brew of poisonous herbs. When the young girl next stepped into the pool, she found herself horribly transformed. Where her lower limbs had been was now a pack of baying hounds. Staring down in horror into the water, she found not one but six heads looking back at her, each one equipped with triple rows of fangs.

Appalled by the change that had come over her, Scylla threw herself from a clifftop into the sea. Poseidon spared her life, so she took up residence in a cave on the tideline, hidden from men's eyes. Her sweet nature had gone with her beauty, and now she had cannibalistic appetites. Henceforth she varied a diet of fish by snatching sailors from passing ships that made the mistake of sailing too close to shore.

Between a rock and a whirlpool

Yet helmsmen had a difficult call to make, for if they steered too far from Scylla they risked succumbing to her fellow-monster Charybdis. According to Homer, she was Poseidon's own daughter by the earth goddess Gaia. Having stolen cattle from Hercules, she was punished by Zeus, who hurled down a thunderbolt that swept her

"Henceforth she varied a diet of fish by snatching sailors from passing ships that made the mistake of sailing too close to shore."

into the depths. There she lived on, unseen, as a fearsome monster, manifesting herself three times daily when she sucked in and then regurgitated vast quantities of seawater. The whirlpool thus created appeared unpredictably in seemingly calm seas, yet was powerful enough to carry entire vessels down to a watery grave.

Ulysses' men learned the dangers of the strait the hard way, when they rowed too close to shore and lost six men to Scylla's terrible heads. The Argonauts were luckier, coming through unscathed. By the time that Aeneas and his crew passed that way following the fall of Troy, Scylla was said to have been transformed by divine intervention into a mighty rock, still to be seen off the Sicilian coast. Yet helmsmen still needed to strike a careful course around her to avoid shipwreck, and the dilemma of steering between Scylla and Charybdis remains a proverbial choice of evils to the present day.

205

CHARYBDIS
Appearance
Unknown, but probably ghastly. All that was ever seen of her was the mighty whirlpool she created.

Size
Unknown.

Lifespan
Cursed by Zeus, so probably immortal.

Powers
Could suck entire ships into her vortex.

Habitat
Under the sea off the Sicilian shore of the Strait of Messina, opposite Scylla.

Merfolk Half-human sea dwellers with tails instead of legs

Appearance
Seafolk having the heads and bodies of humans to the waist, with fishes' lower bodies and tails. According to one description in the *Arabian Nights*, mermaids had "moon faces and hair like a woman's, but their hands and feet were in their bellies and they had tails like fishes".

Size
Usually described as human-sized. A mermaid captured in 1712 off the island of Ambon in the Dutch East Indies (modern Indonesia) was reported to be 59in (about 1.5m) tall.

Lifespan
Unspecified, but not immortal.

Powers
Complete mastery of the undersea realm. Some merfolk were credited with amphibious powers, enabling them to make excursions onto land.

Habitat
Beneath the sea, where they lived (according to Matthew Arnold) in "sand-strewn caverns cool and deep,/Where the winds are all asleep". An Arab tradition had them inhabiting underwater cities.

In 1809 the London *Times* carried an article written by one William Munro, a schoolmaster from Thurso, the northernmost town on the Scottish mainland. He described how, while walking by the coast, he had seen what appeared to be a naked woman sitting on a rock offshore combing her hair. Munro was quick to point out that the same figure was seen by many people besides himself at a distance of no more than 60 feet (20m). One of the other witnesses, a Miss Mackay, described the creature's face as being "round and plump, and of a pinkish hue".

Munro's account joined a long tradition of mermaid sightings for, like ghosts, merfolk have reportedly been spotted by thousands of people down the centuries in many different parts of the world. Well-documented examples have come from, among other places, Iceland, Sri Lanka, Indonesia, Holland, Denmark, the coasts of Suffolk and Ireland, and the Baltic and Antarctic seas. There are also traditions of human–fish hybrids in folklore around the world, from Japan, India and the Arabian Gulf to North America, Mexico and Peru.

From Assyria to ancient Greece
Depictions of merfolk go back to the earliest times. In his ground-breaking excavations at the ancient Assyrian capital of Khorsabad in 1843, Paul-Émile Botta discovered the image of a creature who was half man, half fish, now identified with the Babylonian culture hero Adapa. Similar images came from Syria and the Levantine coast, linked to Dagon and the moon goddess Atargatis. Writing in the nineteenth century, the English folklorist and antiquarian Sabine Baring-Gould saw a connection between the mirrors traditionally carried by mermaids and the full-moon symbol of the latter divinity.

Phoenician images of Atargatis were certainly known to the ancient Greeks, who had their own mythical mermaid in the form of Derceto. Ctesias told the story of how she fell in love with an Assyrian youth and bore his child; throwing herself into a lake in shame, she found her lower body transformed

TRITON, THE MAN—FISH

In the tradition of ancient Greece and Rome, Triton, a monstrous son of the sea god Poseidon, had the upper body of a man and the lower parts of a fish. Scholars have traced his origins to oriental iconography, notably of the Syrian goddess Atargatis, who was shown as half woman and half fish on coins that circulated around the Aegean. A minor deity whose daughter Pallas also came to play a significant part in Greek myth, Triton was usually shown blowing on a conch shell to raise or disperse storms. In later times, he multiplied to create tritons, conch-blowing figures that became a popular motif of classical decorative art.

into the tail of a fish. Classical authors also reported some of the first merfolk sightings. Calling the creatures tritons (see box, above), Pliny the Elder claimed that there was one over 40 feet (12m) long that haunted the Gulf of Cádiz, where it showed a taste for clambering aboard ships at night, sometimes sinking them under its weight.

The Edam mermaid

By medieval times merfolk were often included without special comment in encyclopedic lists of the creatures of the world's oceans, featuring alongside such commonplace marine mammals as porpoises and whales. One well-circulated story told how in 1430 some girls from the Dutch settlement of Edam came across a mermaid floundering in the mud behind a dyke outside the town. They took her home, dressed her in human clothes and taught her to weave, although she never learned to speak intelligibly. The mermaid later moved to the town of Haarlem, where she lived for several years.

A subject for scientific examination

Similar stories continued to crop up over the ensuing centuries. In 1560 the corpses of merfolk caught by fishermen off the coast of Sri Lanka were dissected by a visiting Portuguese surgeon, physician to the Viceroy of Goa, who reported that they were anatomically similar to humans. A scientific work on the sealife of the Molucca Islands, published in 1717, included a detailed account of a "sea wife" 59 inches (1.5m) long, caught off the island of Ambon, who had lived for four days in a vat of water. The creature was said to have had an olive body, webbed fingers and a grey face with seaweed-coloured hair. It squeaked like a mouse and its excrement resembled cat's droppings.

Some of the accounts may have been triggered by out-and-out hoaxes, like the pickled mermaids that at one time used to turn up in fairground sideshows. These were generally produced by sewing the upper parts of monkey corpses to the lower bodies of large fishes. Other sightings almost certainly were cases of mistaken identity. Some may have involved seals, although the more likely candidates were dugongs and manatees, the two remaining members of the Sirenia family of marine mammals, whose closest land-based relative is the elephant. No one could mistake these sea cows, as they are generally known, for the glamorous beings familiar from Hollywood films like *The Little Mermaid* or *Splash*. Yet the big, docile creatures, from 3 feet to 15 feet (1m to 4.5m) in length, can look surprisingly human when glimpsed in the turbid waters where they live, particularly when cradling their young in their flippers, which they use almost like human arms. They also show curiosity, which draws them toward ships, and vocalize through chirps, trills and whistles.

Delightful creatures though they are, sea cows may seem a poor substitute for the merfolk of literature, typically engaged, like Matthew Arnold's Forsaken Merman or Hans Christian Andersen's Little Mermaid herself, in tragic amours with human lovers. Yet for want of any better claimant, they seem the most likely explanation for at least some of the sightings. Some but not all, however, for manatees could hardly explain the Edam mermaid or reports by experienced sailors from seas where sea cows never ventured. In the face of such rationalizations the merfolk still retain some of their mysteries, as endlessly alluring as the hidden depths of the sea.

THE MYSTERY OF MELUSINE

One of the best-loved legends of medieval France told of the lady Melusine, a beautiful fairy maiden who married the mortal Guy, Count of Poitou, and built for him the splendid castle of Lusignan southwest of Poitiers (now destroyed). The one condition she set for their marriage was that he should never disturb her on Saturdays. The couple remained happily married for many years, and Melusine bore her husband several children. Eventually, though, malicious gossips persuaded the count that his wife was concealing some guilty secret in her Saturday sequestrations, leading him to spy on her privacy. He was astonished to see her in her bath, with her upper body as he had always known it but her lower limbs transformed into a fish's tail. Discovering his presence she flew away, never to be seen again. But tradition insisted that in future years, whenever a lord of Lusignan or a king of France was about to die, her ghostly figure would be seen on the ramparts of the castle, wailing over their demise as presciently as any Irish banshee.

⊙ ⊕ ⊖

Kappa Murderous imps that haunted Japan's inland waters

Appearance
Kappas had monkey-like faces, the arms and legs of frogs, and the bodies and shells of tortoises. They were usually depicted with brightly coloured, scaly skin, typically of a yellow or greenish hue. Sometimes their faces had ducks' beaks.

Size
Child-sized.

Lifespan
As spirits, the kappas could be wounded, but apparently not killed.

Powers
An amphibious lifestyle combined with the ability to interact with humans, including the power of speech. They also possessed superhuman strength, allowing them to pull even strong adults below the water's surface.

Habitat
Lakes, ponds and rivers in Japan.

When the American comic-book artists Kevin Eastman and Peter Laird devised Teenage Mutant Ninja Turtles in 1984, the creatures startled Western audiences because of their surrealistic novelty. Yet for a Japanese audience, the concept seemed less far-fetched. Every child there had grown up familiar with kappas, mischievous and sometimes lethal water imps with monkey faces and tortoise bodies combined with the limbs of frogs. Although very different in behaviour and appearance from the US characters, they still bore a close enough resemblance to stir memories of deep-seated childhood fears.

For kappas were terrifying creatures, as anyone who lived near a river or pond in Japan soon learned. Child-sized themselves, they had a particular liking for children – but principally as food. Their favoured delicacies were human entrails, which they obtained by inserting their sinuous paws up the anal passage of their victim and tugging. No wonder, then, that youngsters soon learned not to play in the water if kappas were around. Warning signs were sometimes posted by lakes and ponds where the water spirits were thought to be particularly active.

Not all accounts of kappas, however, were so horrific. In some tales they seemed simply mischievous, but their behaviour easily escalated into positive evil; from passing wind unexpectedly or peering up women's kimonos, they slipped seamlessly into rape or murder. Yet they also had certain redeeming features. Everyone agreed that if a kappa gave its word, it would keep it no matter what the circumstances. They were sticklers for etiquette too, and if they were addressed politely they made a point of responding in kind. And they even had healing powers, being famed for their skill at bone-setting.

They also had an Achilles heel, and crafty mortals learned how to exploit it. Kappas were only able to move around on land because each one had a depression in its head that held a pool of water. If the water was spilled, the kappa was weakened, even to the point of paralysis. Knowing their concern for social correctness, individuals who met a kappa by the wayside were well advised to bow

deeply, knowing that it would inevitably reciprocate, even at the risk of spilling its precious head liquid. In that case the water spirit would be incapacitated, unable to do any further harm.

The hollow in the head was far from the kappa's only oddity. Their diet was equally bizarre, for apart from blood and intestines their favourite food was cucumbers. They were so taken with the vegetables that they were even said to fly about on them, magically endowing them with dragonfly-like wings. Some illustrations of kappas in flight depicted the spirits as almost foetus-like in appearance, leading some researchers to speculate that the legends may have originated in the early Japanese custom of casting stillborn babies into rivers.

Yet the strangest thing of all about the kappa phenomenon was its late survival. Until well into the twentieth century, many people in Japan were genuinely convinced of the creatures' existence. Researchers in some country areas were astonished to find that households preserved legal documents, supposedly signed by kappas, promising not to harm family members. Even today kappa sightings continue to be reported. The Japanese water sprites are evidently still unwilling to be spirited away.

⊙ ⊕ ⊖

Lake Monsters Bunyips and other freshwater beasts

Appearance
Bunyips are usually described as hairy-bodied, with doglike faces, flippers and walrus-like tusks, although an alternative tradition gives them long necks and manes. The classic lake monster is a long-necked creature resembling a prehistoric plesiosaur.

Size
Bunyips are usually said to be the size of small calves or big dogs. Other lake monsters can be much bigger, typically about 25ft (7.5m) long.

Lifespan
Unknown.

Powers
Bunyips have voracious appetites and the strength to pull people and animals down to the depths. All lake monsters are mostly noted for their elusiveness.

Habitat
Bunyips haunt the rivers, creeks, billabongs, swamps and waterholes of Australia. Lake monsters have been reported all over the world, from China to Chile and Canada to the Republic of Congo.

With no wind to ruffle them, the lake waters bask placidly in the sun. A passer-by stops, enchanted by the stillness. A fish rises, tempted by an insect hovering just above the surface, and a tiny ripple moves shoreward, arriving with a gentle plashing at the watcher's feet. Then suddenly, seemingly out of nowhere, something huge emerges from the depths that the startled visitor may spend a lifetime trying to understand or explain …

That scene has played itself out many times in many different lands as unwitting witnesses have found themselves at a loss to account for strange, sometimes terrifying creatures that have unexpectedly revealed themselves from a lake's depths. Canada has its Champ of Lake Champlain (on the US border) and Ogopogo in Lake Okanagan, British Columbia. Congolese river-dwellers speak of the mokele-mbembe that haunts Lake Tele and the surrounding swamps (see page 215). From China come accounts of the Lake Tianchi beast, from Russian the Brosno dragon, from Turkey tales of the monster of Lake Van.

Most famously of all, Scotland boasts several supposed lake creatures, notably Morag from Lake Morar and – still unchallenged in the number of sightings reported and the amount of time, energy and money spent on seeking her out – Nessie of Loch Ness.

Beware of the bunyip

Yet the earliest lake-monster stories came from the other side of the globe and from one of the world's oldest and most long-established peoples, the Aborigines of Australia. The creature they described was in many ways untypical. As depicted in Aboriginal drawings, the bunyip (see illustration, opposite) was generally a hairy creature with a doglike face, together with walrus-like tusks, flippers and a tail. Sometimes it was long-necked, leading some researchers to posit two different varieties.

In legend the bunyip became a bugbear, a bloodthirsty creature always waiting to drag vulnerable people, particularly children, down to the deep. As such, it may have taken on attributes of the saltwater crocodile, a very real threat

"Still unchallenged in the number of sightings reported and the amount of time, energy and money spent on seeking her out is Nessie of Loch Ness."

making occasional, unexpected appearances far inland. Some at least of the bunyip sightings were almost certainly of these creatures, which can grow up to 7 feet 4 inches (2.25m) long and weigh as much as 780 pounds (360kg).

Prehistoric survivals?

The lake monsters reported elsewhere in the world have mostly followed a different pattern. They are usually described as vast – typically up to 25 feet (7.5m) long) – with long, sinuous necks and small heads. Many people have pointed out the similarities between such beings and the plesiosaurs, marine dinosaurs known to have existed in Jurassic and Cretaceous times. Those who believe in the lake monsters' real-life existence mostly like to think of them as prehistoric survivals, rather like the coelacanth, an open-sea fish considered extinct for over 65 million years until a specimen was fished up in the sea off South Africa in 1938.

The continuing search

Many books have been written about the hunt for lake monsters, which has involved a variety of technologies ranging from miniature submersibles and underwater cameras to hydrophones and side-scan sonar. Yet the creatures, if

in some Australian waterways. A more likely clue to its real identity, however, came from its semi-canine features and from the preponderance of sightings reported in bodies of water linked to the great Murray–Darling river system of Victoria, South Australia and New South Wales. Marine fur seals are known to sometimes penetrate the big rivers,

they exist, have proved elusive. Several investigations have turned up unexpected data seeming to indicate something large moving in the depths, but none has yet produced incontrovertible proof as to what the source of the movement might be. The strongest evidence for the existence of Nessie and of her fellows around the world continues to come from the eyewitness accounts of many hundreds of ordinary citizens who claim to have spotted the beasts by chance while going about their ordinary business. In 1934 one such person, a visitor to Loch Ness, took the famous photograph reproduced opposite. At the time it ignited huge excitement, but in recent years experts have dismissed it as an image of an otter or a diving bird – or even of a fake sculpted head attached to a toy submarine.

One day some totally convincing film footage may be taken or some irrefutable biological evidence found to prove once and for all the reality of the lake monsters' existence. Until then, however, they, like the apemen, continue to claim a place in the body of myth.

THE QUEST FOR THE MOKELE-MBEMBE

For more than two centuries stories have come out of central Africa of a huge, long-necked creature said to inhabit remote swamps and waterways of the Congo river system. The most detailed description of the mokele-mbembe or "river-stopper", compiled from eyewitness accounts, was provided by a German army captain who was preparing an official report on the flora and fauna of Cameroon (then a German colony) in 1913. Captain von Stein's account spoke of an animal approximately the size of an elephant with a long, flexible neck and a single tooth or horn. The beast was said to be herbivorous, living off the fruit of a certain type of liana, but was nonetheless dangerous, attacking any boats that approached.

Over the past thirty years a succession of expeditions have visited the region where the mokele-mbembe is supposed to live. They have gathered much material from local people about the creature – including in some cases indications that it is regarded as a spirit rather than a real-life being – but so far have failed to come up with conclusive proof of its existence. Mainstream scientific opinion still tends to regard the mokele-mbembe as mythical, dismissing reported sightings as misidentifications of rhinoceroses (explaining the horn) or else of swimming elephants. Hollywood begged to differ: in the 1985 movie *Baby: Secrets of the Lost Legend*, an American paleontologist and his family discovered an infant mokele-mbembe, identified in the film as the survivor of a lost remnant colony of apatosauruses, and helped protect it from the evil intent of Western hunters.

⊙ ⊕ ⊖

Kraken Colossal, squid-like beast from the deep

Appearance
Vast, with numerous fins and tentacles. Frequently mistaken for a small island; some accounts speak of trees and vegetation growing on its back.

Size
According to Erik Pontoppidan in his *Natural History of Norway*, published in 1754, "its back or upper part … appears to be about a mile and a half (2.5km) in circumference".

Lifespan
Unknown.

Powers
Generally passive, but so vast that any vessel nearby risked being sucked into the vortex created when it submerged. More recent accounts depict it wrapping its tentacles around ships to drag them into the depths.

Habitat
The kraken itself is limited to the waters around Scandinavia, but similar creatures have been reported in many other parts of the world, including the Atlantic Ocean and the Arabian Sea.

Vast, fearsome and hidden in the depths, the kraken has long haunted the imagination of the West. Tennyson wrote a famous poem about it, while John Wyndham borrowed the name for his science-fiction novel *The Kraken Wakes*, proposing a race of deep-sea aliens. More recently the creature made multiple appearances in the film, *Pirates of the Caribbean: Dead Man's Chest*.

In earlier times krakens were taken more seriously. In the 1750s the bishop of Bergen, Erik Pontoppidan, included an account of them in his *Natural History of Norway*. Drawing on sailors' reports, he described the kraken as "round, flat, and full of tentacles", with a back resembling "a number of small islands, surrounded by floating, fluctuating objects that look like seaweed".

From tall tales to hard facts

Stories of living islands come from many cultures. The Celtic St Brendan, whose voyage westward in search of the Isles of the Blessed was the subject of a famous ninth-century work, encountered one, as did Sinbad, as recounted in the *1,001 Nights*. The early Muslim zoologist al-Jahiz wrote of a creature called the zaratan, which some sailors mistook for an island. When they landed on it and lit a fire, the beast sank beneath the waves, drowning all those who could not swim.

In his *Natural History of Molluscs* (1802), the French naturalist Denys de Montfort described the kraken as a colossal octopus, capable of pulling ships down to the depths. His account attracted the attention of a Danish zoologist, Johan Steenstrup, who in the 1850s delivered a number of scientific papers analyzing reported sightings of kraken-like creatures.

Steenstrup's studies coincided with findings of the remains of *Architeuthis dux*, the giant squid. Deep-ocean dwellers, the giant squid are still little known. Current estimates indicating that they can grow up to 45 feet (13m) long, including the tentacles, hardly match the early seafarers' claims. Even so, they are the world's largest invertebrates, and are seen as the most likely reality behind Pontoppidan's stories.

Hydra Swamp serpent with replaceable heads

Appearance
Nine-headed serpent.

Size
Big enough to kill cattle.

Lifespan
Cut short by Hercules, whose second Labour involved killing it.

Powers
Noxious breath and venomous blood, plus the ability to grow extra heads when the existing ones were chopped off.

Habitat
The marshes of Lerna on the Peloponnese peninsula of Greece.

One of Hercules' most daunting labours was the second, which involved confronting the Lernean hydra in a swamp in southern Greece. The beast had been devastating the surrounding area with impunity, for no one dared approach its lair. Part of the monstrous brood born to the serpent-woman Echidna, it was so venomous that even its breath could kill. Worse still, it had a multiplicity of heads, all of which could attack any adversary at the same time.

Hercules was sufficiently alarmed by the prospect to take a helper, his nephew Iolaus. Tracking down the creature in its marshy hideout, he wrapped a cloth around his nose and mouth to protect himself from the fumes before forcing it into the open by shooting fire-arrows into its den. Closing with the creature, he managed to lop off one of its heads with a sword blow, only to learn a terrible lesson: a fresh head grew as soon as the old one was removed.

Hercules solved the problem ingeniously by getting Iolaus to provide him with a supply of burning tree branches. Each time he cut off a head he used one of these brands to cauterize the stump, preventing any fresh growth. Once he had killed the beast by removing all nine heads, he dipped his arrows in the blood flowing from the corpse, leaving them permanently envenomed. By this action the hydra was ultimately avenged, for it was poison from one of Hercules' own arrows, used to shoot down the centaur Nessus, that eventually caused the hero's demise (see page 122).

YAMATA NO OROCHI

Japan had an equivalent of the hydra in Yamata no Orochi, an eight-headed snake killed by the god Susano. Exiled to Earth for trouble-making in heaven, Susano met a weeping couple, who turned out to be earth deities lamenting the fact that they had had to sacrifice seven of their daughters to the monster, which was now coming to consume the eighth and last.

Seeing how beautiful the girl was, Susano offered to kill the beast in return for her hand in marriage. The parents gladly consented, whereupon Susano magically transformed her into a comb that he buried for safety in his long hair. Then he laid out eight vats of rice wine. When the snake arrived, it drank the liquor and collapsed into a drunken stupor. Seizing his opportunity, Susano drew his sword and chopped the monster to pieces before restoring the girl to human form and taking her as his wife.

Sea Serpents Snakelike dwellers of the deep

220

Appearance
One typical example, as described by the captain of HMS *Daedalus* in 1848, was snakelike in form and dark brown in colour, with a white patch at the throat, It had no fins but a seaweed-like mane on its back.

Size
From 30 to 200 ft (10–60m), according to different sources.

Lifespan
Unknown.

Powers
Great speed in the water. According to some sources, the strength to pull small boats down into the depths.

Habitat
The world's oceans.

Covering 71 percent of the globe and still relatively unexplored, the world's oceans are perhaps more likely than any other part of the planet to contain undiscovered creatures. In recent years vessels probing the depths have turned up bizarre beasts – giant tubeworms, deepwater anglerfish with bioluminescent lures – that might well have been viewed as fabulous had there not been good scientific evidence to vouch for their authenticity. So it may be that the sightings of vast, serpentine creatures reported from many different latitudes down the centuries will one day be shown to have contained glimpses of a long-hidden truth.

Such accounts have a long history. The earliest record of sea serpents may come from the Greek philosopher Aristotle, writing in the fourth century BCE. He spoke of creatures living off the coast of Libya that were said to devour oxen on the shore. The Roman writer

Pliny the Elder wrote of a squadron of ships dispatched by Alexander the Great that was beset by creatures more than 30 feet (10m) long as they crossed the Persian Gulf.

Notable Norwegian sightings

Some of the most vivid historical accounts of sea serpents came from Scandinavian sources. In his *History of the Northern People*, published in 1555, Olaus Magnus spoke of a creature 200 feet (60m) long and 20 feet (6m) in girth that lived in sea caves around the Norwegian port of Bergen and came ashore at nights to devour lambs, calves and pigs. Supposedly the beast also sometimes snatched sailors from ships.

Two hundred years later the antiquary Erik Pontoppidan, who became bishop of Bergen, claimed in his *Natural History of Norway* (1752) to have spoken to hundreds of seamen who had regularly seen such creatures. By his account the beasts kept to the seabed for much of the year, but were often spotted at the sea's surface in July and August, their spawning time.

Meanwhile, another Scandinavian ecclesiastic, the Norwegian missionary Hans Egede, who would become known as the "apostle of Greenland", had a first-hand encounter with a bizarre creature while crossing the North Atlantic in 1734. He described a beast that reared up out of the sea, raising its head to the level

> "Pliny the Elder wrote of a squadron of ships dispatched by Alexander the Great that was beset by creatures more than 30 feet (10m) long as they crossed the Persian Gulf."

of the top of the ship's mast. Its body was covered in hard skin, very wrinkled and uneven. The lower part was serpentine in form, and he could see its tail emerging from the waves a ship's length away from the rest of the body.

A close encounter

The crew of a Royal Navy ship, HMS *Daedalus*, saw something similar in the South Atlantic while en route to the remote island of St Helena in 1848. In a subsequent report to the Admiralty, Captain Peter M'Quhae described a serpentine entity whose visible portion was more than 60 feet (18m) in length, although only about 3 feet (1m) in diameter. The creature passed across the ship's stern, "so close under our lee quarter," recorded M'Quhae, "that had it been a man of my acquaintance I should have easily recognized his features with

the naked eye." It held its head about 4 feet (1.3m) above the water, keeping to a steady course at a speed estimated at 12–15 mph (20–25 kph).

Since that time, sightings have continued to crop up from most of the world's oceans, often clustered into groups. One such occurred off Gloucester, Massachusetts, in 1817 (see box, opposite). A beast dubbed the San Clemente monster made repeated appearances between 1914 and 1919 off the California coast, between the San Clemente and Santa Catalina islands in the Santa Barbara Channel. In Britain, there was a spate of reports of a creature dubbed Morgawr ("sea giant" in Cornish) in Falmouth Bay in 1975. Eight years later, several dozen US witnesses described seeing a humped, serpentine beast at least 100 feet (30m) long travelling fast down the California coast.

Incredible ... but true?

Numbering a few hundred in total, eyewitness accounts of sea serpents vary in their detail, and researchers who have analysed them have come to the conclusion that they describe several different types of creature. The French cryptozoologist Bernard Heuvelmans suggested nine separate varieties, including creatures resembling giant sea-lions and eels, a father-of-all-the-turtles, a super-otter, a vast marine saurian (crocodile), a giant invertebrate, a many-humped creature only known from the North Atlantic, a multi-finned creature thought to be a prehistoric cetacean survival, and a merhorse, described as a pinniped with a horse-like head. Other suggestions have ranged from giant sharks (perhaps descended from the prehistoric megalodon) to surviving populations of Steller's sea-cow, a larger relative of the dugong and manatee that measured as much as 25 feet (7.5m) and weighed up to 6 tonnes and is thought to have become extinct in the eighteenth century.

Sceptics of course reject all such possibilities and instead seek alternative explanations in misidentifications of known creatures or nautical phenomena. Reports of many-humped beasts could, they suggest, actually refer to porpoises jumping in line. Accounts of creatures with seaweed-coloured manes might in fact describe large floating clumps of seaweed. Marine biologists have claimed that many of the stories may have been inspired by oarfish, rarely seen deep-sea dwellers that have been known to grow up to 36 feet (11m) in length. While all of these suggestions might explain some of the phenomena observed, many cases still remain difficult to account for. The possibility of major discoveries yet to emerge from the ocean depths remains very real.

223

THE GLOUCESTER SIGHTINGS

Over seventeen days in August 1817, more than a hundred people witnessed a giant sea serpent in the waters off Gloucester, Massachusetts, a small fishing port north of Boston. The accounts described a snakelike creature variously estimated as between 40 and 150 feet (13–45m) in length, with a head "as broad as a horse or more so, but not quite as long", according to one witness, or the size of a "four-gallon keg", according to another. Most of the spectators saw the beast from the harbour walls or from the shore, but some boats also went out in pursuit. A ship's carpenter on one of them claimed to have got within 30 feet (10m) of the monster, at which point he shot at it with his rifle. Although he thought he had hit its head, the creature passed under his boat and swam off at great speed, undulating vertically in the water "like a caterpillar". Gaffney estimated that it was moving at between 20 and 30 mph (30–50 kph).

A local scientific group, the Linnaean Society, subsequently investigated the phenomenon. Presented with an odd-looking snake found at the time on shore, they proudly announced it to be a baby sea serpent. Their account was promptly debunked by European scientists, who correctly identified the creature as an ordinary black snake with a deformed spine. The society's error served to discredit the whole story of the Gloucester sea serpent – perhaps unfairly, for many of the first-person accounts remain hard to explain away.

Sirens   Bird–maidens whose song lured sailors to their death

Appearance
Birds with the heads, upper bodies and sometimes arms of beautiful women.

Size
Usually portrayed the size of large birds.

Lifespan
Legend held that they died when the spell cast by their singing failed to work.

Powers
A gift of enchantment linked to their entrancing song.

Habitat
A Mediterranean coast close to the island of the enchantress Circe. One ancient tradition placed them on Capri, off the coast of southern Italy.

According to Suetonius, the emperor Tiberius used to sardonically tease scholars by asking them to tell him the song the sirens sang. For the music the bird–women made was not just beautiful on the ear, it also contained the sum of human wisdom. So at least Homer implied, when he made one of them tell Ulysses: "We know all things that come to pass on the bounteous Earth."

Famously, Ulysses could hear their blandishments because he had had himself strapped to the mast of his ship, having stopped the ears of his sailors with beeswax. The enchantress Circe had warned him to take these steps, for any mariner who heard the song was irresistibly impelled to throw himself overboard. Jason and the Argonauts also managed to escape their lures, in their case because they had the sweet-voiced Orpheus aboard. He made such beautiful music that he eclipsed the sirens who, in despair at the rebuff, supposedly plunged to their death on the boulders below.

Sources differed on the number of sirens: some suggested two, others three, and there were even variant traditions counting up to five. They were said to be daughters of the sea god Phorcys (or the river god Achelous) and of the muse Terpsichore. At one time Hera persuaded them to test their musical skills against the nine Muses, but they lost the contest. The Muses then vindictively plucked the sirens' feathers to make themselves victory wreaths.

Legend maintained that the sirens were born human. Companions of the goddess Persephone, they acquired their wings so they could search for her following her abduction by Hades, lord of the Underworld. Thereafter they took up residence by the sea. Various localities claimed them, but the most persistent traditions placed them in Campania, either on the island of Capri itself or on the mainland coast opposite.

In later times the sirens became symbols of female enticement, excoriated by Christian moralists as temptresses or demons. Yet the memory of their music always retained its magic. Even today, the sirens' song conveys an image of unattainable beauty, one that remains destructive in its otherworldly power.

Nagas Serpent demi-gods of India

Appearance
Cobra-like snakes, sometimes with seven heads, that could also take human form.

Size
Variable, but usually portrayed as very large.

Lifespan
Semi-divine, hence potentially limitless. One tradition told how their ancestors conquered death by licking up drops of the elixir of immortality.

Powers
Guardians of springs, wells and rivers, they also protected treasure and preserved esoteric knowledge. Could bring rain and floods.

Habitat
India, where they lived underwater (or in some traditions underground) in splendid palaces studded with jewels.

226

Nagas were powerful water-spirits of Indian myth conceived in the form of snakes. Feared and venerated over many centuries, they became the objects of a complex and sometimes contradictory body of legend. Tales of nagas were told not just in India itself but also in Nepal, Burma, Indonesia, Malaysia and even Cambodia, where naga imagery featured in the temples of Angkor Wat.

The legend of the forked tongue

Ancient Hindu tradition made the nagas subjects of the 100-headed serpent god Vasuki, a symbol of eternity. Vishnu himself was often pictured lying on Vasuki's back in the cosmic waters, resting after his primordial act of creation. Vasuki also played a central role in the Hindu myth of the churning of the milk ocean, serving as a rope, twisted around the holy mountain of Mandara, to tumble the liquid in search of soma, the elixir of life. Later legend maintained that the nagas took the opportunity to lick up some of the soma, thereby guaranteeing themselves immunity from death. At the same time, though,

they cut their tongues on the grass, which is why serpents have ever since had forked tongues.

Thereafter the nagas retreated to the waters, serving as attendants to Varuna, god of rivers, oceans and storms. Some, the naga-rajas, served as local deities presiding over lakes or rivers from jewel-encrusted underwater palaces where they reclined amid dancing and singing and flowers. Like dragons in other traditions, they also guarded treasures.

A battle of wits

Besides their significant role in the Hindu canon, nagas also featured strongly in Buddhist tradition. Buddhist legend told of a longstanding enmity between the snake spirits and the garudas (see pages 26–27), the giant, eagle-headed birds of Indian myth. The garudas hunted the nagas for food until the serpents learned to swallow rocks that made them too heavy for the birds to carry. One Buddhist sage then won the birds' favour by teaching them to seize nagas by the tail, thereby forcing them to vomit up the protective stones.

Longwang China's dragon lords of the waters

Appearance
Their true form was as scaled dragons with serpentine bodies and heads adorned with horns and whiskers, but they often chose to appear in human guise.

Size
Typically 3 or 4 miles (5–6.5km) long, although tradition held that, if he so wished, a dragon king could make himself as large as the entire universe.

Lifespan
Immortal.

Powers
Vast, including stirring up typhoons and whirlpools when they rose to the sea's surface and creating storms when they took to the air.

Habitat
Beneath the water in splendid palaces, where they fed on opals and pearls.

In the Chinese classic *The Journey to the West*, best known in English in Arthur Waley's translation as *Monkey*, the eponymous monkey hero wanted a weapon that would make him invincible. He knew where to look – at the court of one of the four Dragon Kings, masters of the seas. So he journeyed to the palace home of the greatest of them all – the King of the Eastern Sea. There, deep under the waters of the East China Sea, he duly purloined a magic wand that could change size from a tiny twig to a trunk long enough to reach up to Heaven.

With his new acquisition, Monkey was able to rule over all the simian race. Yet he had made a dangerous enemy. Enraged at the theft, the Dragon King went to the Lord of Hell to complain, and when that avenue failed to produce the desired results he took his grievance to the Jade Emperor who ruled over Heaven itself. Monkey duly found himself summoned before the celestial presence, where – to keep him out of further trouble – he was given a menial job with the resounding title of Grand Master of the Heavenly Stables.

As the story suggested, China's long-wang or dragon kings were both mighty and well connected. The greatest of them were four in number, and between them they ruled the world's oceans: northern, eastern, western and southern. Immortal themselves, they answered to nobody but the Jade Emperor himself, and lesser beings crossed them at their peril. It was a measure of Monkey's cosmic chutzpah that he dared risk such a foolhardy feat – and had the nerve and ingenuity to carry it through to a successful conclusion.

A mark of authority

Stories of the longwang drew upon a long Chinese tradition of dragons as symbols of royal power. The fabulous culture heroes that populated the country's legendary history drew heavily on this association. Fuxi, the first of China's mythical Three Sovereigns and the being who taught the Chinese how to cook and to fish with nets, was said to have had a serpent's body. Huang Di, the Yellow Emperor, from whom all later Chinese traced their ancestry, turned into a

splendour in magnificent seabed palaces, adorned with jewels and guarded by shrimp soldiers commanded by crab generals. They had shape-shifting powers, and generally chose to appear to people in human guise, royally attired but sometimes with a dragon face.

Big dragons in small ponds

Yet few mortals had dealings with these great eminences, who ranked high within the ranks of China's pantheon of gods. Most encounters with longwang were with local lords who ruled over smaller bodies of water – individual rivers, lakes or ponds. They too could be highly influential beings. They were held to control clouds and rain, serving as weather as well as water gods. In a land as prone to drought and floods as China, their powers gave them a life-or-death hold over all who lived nearby.

Towns and villages across the nation, particularly those located close to a large river or the sea coast, had temples to the local dragon king, where priests would conduct rites and ordinary people would make offerings to avert droughts and prevent lethal flooding. Early in Chinese history, a young girl was for many centuries thrown into the Yellow River as an annual sacrifice to the longwang who ruled the waterway, still

dragon at the end of his life to ascend into Heaven; as a result, the Chinese themselves are sometimes called "descendants of the dragon". In later times the historic emperors of China sat on the Dragon Throne. The dragon symbol became largely standardized and was rendered in all kinds of media, including silk (see above) and ceramic tiles (see opposite). Under the Qing or Manchu Dynasty, which ruled from 1644 to 1912, it was a capital offence for commoners to wear garments embroidered with the emblem, for to do so was to commit the crime of lèse-majesté.

It was only fitting, then, that the dragon lords of the oceans lived in

known as "China's sorrow" for the millions of victims of its frequent floods.

These lesser rulers too could be fearsome, as much for their unpredictability as for their power. Folktales told of Qian Tang, the Dragon Lord of the South, who was famous for his temper – so much so that to restrain him, Shangdi, the ruler of Heaven, had him shackled in the dungeons of his brother, the dragon lord of Dongting Lake.

One day a human visitor found his way to the lord's underwater palace bearing a message. The man, a poor scholar, had been given the commission by a beautiful girl whom he met lamenting by the banks of the River Qing.

The scholar was magically wafted down to the depths and ushered into the lord's presence. As the ruler, who had taken human form to greet his visitor, read the message, his countenance darkened. For the girl was his daughter, and the letter described how her husband, the dragon king of the River Qing, was mistreating her.

This was a job for Qian Tang. Freed from his chains, he set off to take vengeance. Soon he was back with the girl at his side, having killed and eaten her abusive husband and, incidentally, caused a flood in the river valley that killed some 60,000 people. Even so, when he

expressed remorse for this deed, Shangdi proved willing to forgive him, restoring him to his former position.

In many ways the longwang, with their fabulous underwater residences and unpredictable interventions in human affairs, recalled the naga-rajas of Indian legend (see pages 226–227). Yet they also acquired a special cachet of their own from the long-standing Chinese veneration of dragons. Their presence still lingers on today in the sport of dragon-boat racing, practised across the Chinese world in canoe-like vessels whose prows and bows are proudly adorned with the heads and tails of longwang.

Kelpie Water horses that drown the unwary in the depths

Appearance
Seemingly identical to a normal horse.

Size
Horse-sized.

Lifespan
As spirits, potentially limitless.

Powers
Shape-shifting, including the ability to take human form if they chose. Supernatural strength, together with magical powers to control the elements.

Habitat
Scotland, in the vicinity of rivers and lochs. Similar creatures were also found in Wales, Ireland and the Scandinavian lands.

Visitors to the Scottish lochs would be advised to beware of the kelpie. "Every lake has its Kelpie or Water horse, often seen by the shepherd sitting upon the brow of a rock, dashing along the surface of the deep or browsing upon the pasture on its verge", wrote Patrick Graham, vicar of Aberfoyle south of the Trossachs in his *Sketches of Perthshire* in 1806. In the same work he recorded the local belief that one of his predecessors in the parish, the Rev. Robert Kirke, had not died when he left the mortal world in 1691 but had instead gone to Fairyland, having been received into the Otherworld while walking over a fairy mound located outside the village.

The most malicious of mounts

The kelpies of which the pastor wrote were freshwater spirits that generally took the form of handsome chestnut horses. They were shape-shifters, though, and their nature was malicious. Their favourite trick was to wait, saddled and bridled, by the roadside, hoping to attract the attention of some weary pedestrian. If a traveller was unwise enough to

POSEIDON'S CHARIOT-BEARERS

The classical world had its own water horses in the form of hippocamps, the legendary creatures said to have pulled the golden chariot of the mighty Poseidon. The fancy probably originated in the fact that the deity was god of horses as well as of the sea. Poseidon's mounts had the foreparts of horses attached to the scaly hindquarters of serpentine fishes (see illustration, opposite). The Romans also made similar claims for their sea god Neptune, although they may have drawn on native Italian traditions in doing so. Drawings of winged water horses have been found in Etruscan tombs, where their function was perhaps to suggest supernatural beings carrying the souls of the departed by water to the Otherworld.

Despite their unlikely physiology, hippocamps became a favourite subject for artists and sculptors in classical and later times. Some fine Baroque examples are still regularly admired by visitors to the eighteenth-century Trevi Fountain, a favourite tourist sight in Rome.

mount one, it would at once take off at a whirlwind pace and plunge into the depths of a nearby river or loch. As its tail hit the water there would be a sound like thunder and a blinding light. Horse and rider would never be seen again.

Storm-bringing shape-shifters

Kelpies also had other ways of doing harm. One tradition claimed they could swallow people up, boots, braces and all. They were said to give warning of com-ing storms by their neighing, and were sometimes blamed for bringing them on. It was also held that they could cause lakes or rivers to overflow their banks, sweeping away passers-by to their death in the flood. The spirits could even appear in human guise, usually taking the form of unkempt men who leaped up into the saddle behind lone horse-men, seizing the reins and taking horse and rider for wild rides that sometimes caused their victims to die of fright.

233

> "It would carry its prey to the depths, where it would swallow them up, leaving only the liver to float to the water's surface in a bloody wake."

As so often, however, folktales also commemorated canny individuals who managed to get the better of the troublesome spirits. One told of a certain Graham of Morphie, a village in Aberdeenshire, who needed cheap labour to help him build a new manor house. He soon thought of the kelpie that dwelled in the neighbouring loch, knowing that, like some genie from the *1001 Nights*, it possessed preternatural strength. He was aware too that humans could gain control over a kelpie if they could snatch its bridle, in which much of its magic power was concentrated.

To carry out his scheme, the laird first took the precaution of protecting his existing home with a cross of rowan wood, knowing no evil spirit could thereafter cross its threshold. Then he crept up on the kelpie as it stood by the roadside waiting for prey. Before the creature realized what was happening, he had cut off its bridle with a thrust of his broadsword.

As Graham had suspected, the kelpie's first instinct was to rush to his house to wreak havoc, only to find itself thwarted by the cross above the front door. Crestfallen, it then had no option but to accept his terms: that the bridle would only be returned if the creature carried the stones needed for the new house to the site where it was to be built.

It was back-breaking work, and any normal horse would have died from exhaustion long before it was completed. Even the kelpie wasted away carrying load after load, and was little more than a shadow of itself by the time the task was completed. Although he had been a hard taskmaster, the laird fulfilled his part of the bargain by returning the bridle.

The kelpie's curse
But the kelpie got its revenge. Before it galloped away it cursed him and his family, chanting: "Sair back and sair bones/Driving the Laird o' Morphie's stones!/The Laird o'Morphie ne'er will thrive/While this kelpie is alive!" And the words came true, for little good came to the Grahams from their splendid new home. Misfortune dogged their steps, and before many generations had passed the line had died out completely.

Kelpies were specifically Scottish – the name is thought to derive from *calpach*, Gaelic for "colt" – but they had their equivalents in other lands. The Welsh equivalent was the *ceffyl dwr*, said to be able to fly, while in Ireland people spoke of the *augisky*, which was relatively safe to ride inland but turned into a ravening beast at the first scent of water, dragging its hapless rider under the surface to his doom.

An object of fear and loathing

This creature in turn had its origins in an alternative Scottish tradition of the *each uisge* ("water horse"), a cannibalistic monster of the Highland sea lochs and coastal waters. While the kelpie was dangerous but also in some ways alluring, the *each uisge* mostly inspired fear and loathing. One particularly alarming aspect was that it could take human form, appearing as a handsome man to attract women victims. It would carry its prey to the depths, where it would swallow them up, leaving only the liver to float to the water's surface in a bloody wake. To avoid such a fate, maidens were warned to observe strangers carefully, checking to see if they had a salt-sea smell to them or wisps of seaweed in their hair.

In Scandinavia a parallel legend spoke of the *bäckahäst* or "brook horse", a malevolent water spirit in the form of a handsome white stallion. Like its Scottish counterpart, the *bäckahäst* would appear to lone travellers, often in foggy weather. Any who climbed on its back would be unable to get off again and would be carried off to a watery grave in the nearest stream or river.

Scandinavian myth also had a separate tradition of horse-headed sea monsters, variously described as lindworms or *havhest* ("sea horses") – also the name given to the gull known as the fulmar. Vast creatures big enough to sink ships, these were said to boast equine heads with glaring eyes and flowing manes attached to the lower bodies of serpents. One modern Scandinavian folklorist has sought to trace all reports of sea serpents back to these saltwater sea horses, maintaining that later descriptions of ichthyosaur-like creatures were a distortion of the tradition post-dating the discovery and widespread publicizing of dinosaur bones in the nineteenth century.

235

Nix Seductive water spirits of European legend

Appearance
German nix and
Slav rusalki normally
took the form of
freshwater mermaids
who lured men to
death by drowning. The
Scandinavian näcken
were more often male
spirits who attracted
people with their
enchanting music.

Size
Apparently human.

Lifespan
As spirit beings, the
nix were not subject
to ageing or mortality.

Powers
Shape-shifting, plus
an irresistible allure,
whether through their
beauty or their music.

Habitat
Lakes and rivers of
the northern and Slavic
lands.

The folklore of Germany, Scandinavia and the Slavic lands was rich in stories of malign water spirits that tempted unwary humans to their deaths. All were shape-shifters who could change their form at will, but German nix usually appeared as beautiful women, albeit with mermaid tails concealed below the water's surface. A less flattering tradition maintained they were really crones with green hair, skin and teeth who used magic powers merely to create the illusion of beauty.

All versions agreed that nix interacted with the human world, sometimes taking on the guise of old women to go

to market. Observant people could spot them by some telltale trait, typically a wet hem to their garments. They were also said to keep cattle in the riverside meadows, and the beasts were famous for their sleek, well-fed appearance. Nix were always dangerous, for they rarely missed a chance to drag people down to their dwellings beneath the water. Their victims were never seen living again, although their drowned bodies might later be found by grieving relatives. There were stories too of nix coming ashore to live with mortal husbands, but the tales always ended unhappily. After a time the lure of the water would become too great, and the spirit wife would abandon the family home, leaving a pool of blood-red water to mark her going.

The Scandinavian equivalent of the nix was the näcken, a male spirit who attracted women and children to their deaths by playing enchanted airs on his fiddle. Typically, he took the form of a handsome young man, and he was thought to be at his busiest on Midsummer Night and Christmas Eve.

The most developed body of legend, however, concerned the rusalka of the Slavic lands. These mainly female beings were the spirits of the unquiet dead: babies who had gone to the grave unbaptized, girls who had drowned, or

---

THE LORELEI

Easily the most famous of the German nix was the Lorelei, immortalized in a poem by Heinrich Heine. Tradition claimed she was originally a human girl, jilted by a faithless lover, who threw herself into the River Rhine in despair and was transformed into a nix. Thereafter she got her revenge on the human race by sitting on the imposing Lorelei rock near the town of St Goarshausen, and distracting passing sailors with her beauty. The spot where the rock stands is in fact the narrowest point on the river north of the Swiss border, made dangerous by underwater obstacles and strong currents. Many sailors have come to grief there over the centuries – victims, if the legend is to be believed, of the nix's fatal allure.

---

died for love. They emerged from rivers or lakes at night, when they could be seen dancing in the water-meadows by moonlight. Many a man was tempted to join them, and those who succumbed would disappear forever to a new life in the marvellous river- or lake-bed mansions in which the spirits lived.

The rusalkas' power was so great that villagers devoted a whole week in early June to laying them to rest. At that time, swimming was forbidden. Instead, people would decorate their houses and surrounding trees with garlands and stage dances at which courtships were started and marriages arranged. There would also be services to bring peace to the troubled souls, and the festivities would end with the effigy of a rusalka being consigned to a nearby river.

⊙ ⊕ ⊖

Selkie Shape-shifting seal people of the northern lands

Appearance
Seals that could shed
their skins to take
human form.

Size
Seal-sized.

Lifespan
Unspecified, but
approximately human.

Powers
Shape-shifting – but
only so long as they had
access to their seal skin.

238

Habitat
Offshore waters of the
Orkney Islands, northern
and western Scotland,
Ireland and Iceland.

Anyone who has watched seals in the seas offshore has likely been struck by how human they can seem. Mammals like us, they show a curiosity and playfulness that strikes a chord of sympathy that crosses the barrier of species. So it is maybe not surprising that communities living by seal-infested waters should have developed legends of selkies – seals that could literally anthropomorphize, taking on the appearance of men and women by shedding their seal skins.

The word itself comes from *selch*, the Orcadian term for "seal". Most of the stories follow a pattern, drawing on the fact that selkies who had taken human form needed the skins if they were to return to their ocean home. Anyone who purloined the skin therefore had the selkie in their power; and as the creatures were famous for their beauty when they assumed human guise, many people chose to make them their partners. Women took selkie husbands and men selkie wives, and often the unions were long-lasting and blessed with children.

Yet the sea was so much a part of the selkies' being that they always pined for it and, as in similar stories of merfolk, could rarely resist a chance to return

---

THE BISHOP FISH

In 1531 a strange prodigy was seen off the coast of Poland, near the German border. It was a marine creature said at the time to resemble a bishop. A contemporary engraving shows a beast with two froglike legs, a pointed head vaguely reminiscent of a mitre, and a capelike projection on the back rather like the wings of a ray. To complete the likeness, the illustrator gave the beast two finny hands, one apparently raised in blessing.

This peculiar entity was taken alive and presented to King Sigismund I of Poland who, considering it to be in distress, ordered it to be returned to the sea. Commenting on the incident in his *Book of Beasts*, the English writer T.H. White, author of *The Once and Future King*, said of the creature: "Perhaps he was a walrus, for some bishops have looked like decayed walruses, but the matter is now beyond conjecture".

if one showed up. One day the selkie would discover its long-hidden skin and then, turning its back on home, spouse and family, would opt instead for life with its own kind sporting in the waves.

The kindness of strangers

Another group of stories told of cross-species debts of gratitude and acts of kindness repaid. A typical tale of this genre recounted how a crofter once found a cow seal giving birth to a pup on the seashore, and was minded to keep the youngster as a pet for his own children, who lived by an inland loch nearby. But the mother seal was so evidently distraught at the prospect of losing her infant that he took pity on her and returned the cub.

Seven years later, when his son and two daughters were gathering limpets one late afternoon in a cliff-bound cove between two headlands, they found themselves in danger of being cut off by the rising tide. Just when their plight seemed hopeless, two grey-cloaked women appeared suddenly, as if from nowhere, to carry them to safety through the waves. Having set them unharmed on dry land around the spit, the strangers bade them farewell, giving them a message for their father: "One spared to the sea is three spared to the land."

The children duly ran home to tell their story, pausing only briefly to see which way their rescuers had gone. There were no women to be seen, but far out to sea two seals were swimming side by side into the deepening twilight.

Ahuizotl Aztec water-dog that drowned its victims

Appearance
Doglike, with small, pointed ears, a shiny black coat, and a long tail equipped with a hand at the end.

Size
The size of a small dog.

Lifespan
Unknown.

Powers
Strength to pull adult humans underwater.

Habitat
Freshwater rivers and lakes in the Aztec lands of North America.

Many mythical beasts are known only from ancient texts, but the task of identifying them becomes even harder when the manuscripts come from a suppressed culture. So it is with the ahuizotl, a mysterious creature regarded with fear by the Aztec people of Mexico, whose world was destroyed by Spanish conquistadors in the sixteenth century.

The ahuizotl is known from a single source, the *Florentine Codex*. This work, drawn up under the supervision of a Franciscan missionary in the years after the conquest, sought to preserve details of Aztec culture at a time when it was being eradicated in favour of Christian ideology imposed by the Spanish.

The reference to the ahuizotl described a creature resembling a small, smooth-haired dog with pointed ears. The beast's oddest feature was a long tail equipped with an extension "just like a human hand". It used this fist to seize people who approached its haunts in rivers and lakes, pulling them under the surface to drown. It then ate their eyes, teeth and nails, leaving the rest of the body intact but covered with bruises. The creature was also said to make whimpering sounds, "as though a small child was crying".

Similar creatures have been found in the folklore of neighbouring peoples. The Hopi of New Mexico had stories of a water-dog, while the Shasta of northern California also spoke of aquatic creatures "like huge spotted dogs" that pulled people down to their death in the waters. To find any parallel to the ahuizotl's hand, however, researchers have had to look as far as the Araucanians of southern Chile and Argentina, who told stories of a prehensile-tailed creature called the nurufilu, or fox–serpent.

The Araucanian legends seem to refer to some sort of otter, and an otter of some kind remains the most likely origin of stories of the ahuizotl. Yet the Aztecs were aware of the Neotropical river otter, *Lontra longicaudis*, the only species now found in Mexico, which gets a separate entry in the *Florentine Codex* under the name of aitzcuintli. For them the ahuizotl was something else again, but whether a different, perhaps now lost otter species or some mere figment of imagined fears it is now too late to tell.

A Miscellany of Monsters

Like the world's real-life fauna, the mythical bestiary contains many local variants and subspecies. This miscellany features a selection of the better known or more distinctive examples.

⊙ Peryton

In his *Book of Imaginary Beings*, the Argentinian man of letters Jorge Luis Borges included an entry on perytons (see below), described as hybrid creatures with a deers' head and body and the wings of a bird. Supposedly they flew in flocks and were mortal foes of the human race, sometimes swooping down to slaughter people in substantial numbers. Oddly, they cast a human shadow.

Borges's supposed source was a manuscript copied by a sixteenth-century Sephardic rabbi from the work of a Greek scholiast (commentator on classical literature), who himself had taken the details from the oracles of the Sibyl of Erythraea, lost when the great library of Alexandria in Egypt burned down in the year 642 CE. No other mention of the peryton has ever been found, however, and today it is generally assumed that the creature's only true pedigree lay in Borges's inventive imagination and fondness for scholarly jokes.

⊙ Huma

Sometimes called the Persian phoenix, the huma actually had more in common with the Chinese fenghuang (see pages 36–37) as a bird of good omen, bringing blessings on all on whom its shadow fell. Anyone lucky enough to have one perch, however briefly, on his

242

head could expect to become a king. By nature compassionate, the huma shunned predation, feeding instead on carrion. Again like the fenghuang, it had an identity that crossed genders, although in its case it was said to have a male half and a female half, one leg and one wing being of each sex. The huma was also known in India, where it was associated with the bird of paradise.

☉ Alan

Winged spirits of Filipino legend that supposedly stole umbilical cords, menstrual blood and miscarried foetuses in order to fashion living human babies that they then raised as their own.

☉ Hamsa

Literally meaning "goose" or "swan", the hamsa of Hindu myth was a gigantic bird of good omen that served as Brahma's mount and was also associated with the goddess Saraswati.

⊕ Humbaba

The forest guardian killed by Gilgamesh and his companion Enkiddu in the Akkadian *Epic of Gilgamesh*, the world's oldest literary work. Living in the cedar woods of Lebanon, Humbaba was said to have a lion's head on a giant's body: "When he roars it is like the torrent of the storm, his breath is like fire, and his jaws are death itself."

⊕ Dybbuk

A malicious, wandering spirit of Jewish legend with the power to make its home in a human victim's mind, creating a distinct personality separate from the possessed person's own. Dybbuks were said to be the souls of sinners that had escaped from Gehenna, the final abode of the wicked.

⊕ Lady Midday

A Slavic spirit taking the form of a young woman clothed in white who roamed the fields when the sun was hottest, afflicting farmhands with headaches and fainting fits. Poludnica, as she was known in Polish and Russian, is now generally viewed as a personification of sunstroke. A related spirit from the German state of Brandenburg was the Roggenmuhme or Lady of the Rye, who abducted children as they wandered among the high grasses on hot summer days. Lady Midday should not be confused with the Demon of the Noontide, which afflicted the desert fathers of the early Church and was associated with accidie, a sense of cosmic purposelessness said to affect sufferers most strongly in the middle of the day.

⊕ Azhi Dahaka

A triple-headed serpent that personified evil in the Zoroastrian tradition. Legend held that Azhi Dahaka (see above) had reigned over the world for a thousand years until finally vanquished by the hero Thraetona. Seeking to kill the monster, Thraetona struck it with his sword, only to release from the wounds a flood of verminous creatures that threatened to submerge the Earth. On divine advice, he staunched the flow by binding the serpent and imprisoning it under Mount Demavend in the Elburz Mountains. And there it will remain until the final cataclysm when, like Jormungand in Norse myth (see page 203), it will finally burst its bonds, sweeping away a third of humankind before it is finally dispatched by the saviour figure Keresaspa.

⊕ La Llorona

Known across Central America, Mexico and in Spanish-speaking communities of the US South, La Llorona – meaning "the weeping woman" – was a banshee-like figure whose appearance was said to presage death. Legend held that she was the ghost of a despairing wife who chose to drown herself and her children after being abandoned by her husband or lover. Her spectral figure was thereafter fated to wander the banks of the lake or river where she died, eternally looking for her lost infants, and her anguished cries could be heard piercing the darkness on moonless nights. Mothers particularly dreaded meeting her, for she was sometimes said to take other people's babies to replace her own.

⊕ Tiyanak

Tiyanaks were demon children in Filipino folklore – or, more correctly, spirits that took the form of children to lure unwary humans into their clutches. Typically, one might lie on the forest floor crying like a baby. Anyone warm-hearted enough to offer help would quickly find that the supposed infant sprouted fangs and claws. Another tradition held that tiyanaks were actually wizened, gnome-like creatures who could perfectly imitate the sound of distressed children but whose real nature quickly became apparent from close up.

⊕ Rokurokubi

To all appearances normal humans by day, rokurokubi (see right) had the ability to stretch their necks to extraordinary lengths by night. These Japanese spirits could crane their heads, attached to the body by an infinitely extensible umbilical cord of flesh, into adjoining houses or the street to spy on neighbours, whom they liked to frighten by assuming the fierce grimaces of the oni (see below).

⊕ Oni

The oni were Japanese ogres – huge, unkempt beings with clawed hands and two horns growing from their foreheads. Their skin was often boldly coloured, red, blue, black and green being the most common shades. They wore tiger skins to hide their nakedness and clutched fearsome iron clubs crowned with spikes; the phrase "an oni with an iron club" became proverbial, meaning someone or something already strong made invincible by an additional source of power.

Like their Western counterparts, oni served in Japanese folk tales as dumb but fearsome villains who could be tamed or overcome by the agile wits of their opponents. One such story told how a benevolent deity sought to save the inhabitants of a valley from the depradations of a pair of cannibalistic oni by offering the couple a challenge. If they could build a flight of 100 steps up to his shrine in the course of a single

night, he would personally see that a human victim was brought daily to their door. If they failed, though, they were to leave the villagers in peace.

Thanks to their great strength, the two had little difficulty in raising the steps, and they set the ninety-ninth in place with the night barely halfway through. Then they suddenly froze as a strident cock-crow echoed through the darkness. Disconsolately they trudged home, convinced that they had failed to meet the deadline – leaving the god, who had mimicked the bird's cry, laughing to think that anything so big could be so easily fooled.

⊕ Chichevache

Literally "starved cow", the chichevache was an ironical beast mentioned by Chaucer that only survived by eating virtuous women and hence was chronically malnourished.

⊕ Tsukumogami

In Japanese folklore, household objects could take on a life of their own once they became 100 years old. They then became tsukumogami, the name given to a whole class of semi-comic spirits, from animated sandals and umbrellas to itinerant paper scrolls and tea-kettles, whose nearest Western equivalents are found in Disney cartoons like the Sorcerer's Apprentice episode of *Fantasia*.

⊖ Makara

In Hindu myth, a celestial creature often represented as a hybrid with the head of a crocodile and the body and tail of a fish. The makara (see below) was best known as the mount of Varuna, a sky god who was also associated with rain and with the celestial ocean. It was additionally linked with Ganga, goddess of the Ganges, in which role it perhaps recalled the freshwater dolphins that are

still found in the river's waters, although now increasingly endangered.

⊖ Dobhar-Chu

Now simply Gaelic for "otter", the dobhar-chu of legend was a fearsome beast given to attacking humans. One supposedly killed a woman named Grace McGloughlan at Lough Glenade in County Leitrim in 1722. A local ballad described how her husband shot the creature when he found it feeding on her corpse, thereby drawing its mate from the lake. A chase ensued that ended with the second dobhar-chu also being killed several miles away. The woman is buried in Conwell churchyard, reportedly beneath a gravestone bearing an image of an otter-like beast, although time has now removed all trace of the accompanying lettering.

⊖ Korrigans

The korrigans were Breton equivalents of the sirens, beautiful maidens who haunted wells and inland waters and tempted men with their singing. Although not normally winged, they could change shape at will and had foreknowledge of the future. Like other Celtic fairy mistresses, they were fatally attractive to mortals; those who fell in love with them wasted away and died, for

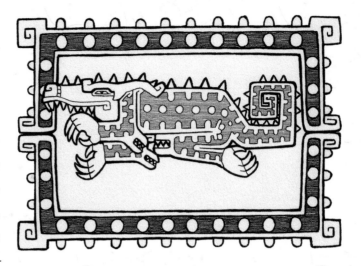

the korrigans drew sustenance from the souls of their lovers. They were fond too of stealing babies, leaving malformed changelings in their place to leer up blankly at their astonished mothers.

⊖ Cipactli

The word for "caiman" in the Nahuatl language, Cipactli (see above) was also the name given to a crocodile-like monster that fought Tezcatlipoca in an Aztec creation myth, biting off the god's foot when he used it as bait to draw the creature to land.

⊖ Encantado

Literally "the enchanted", encantados in Brazilian folklore were river dolphins with the power to take human form and to interact with people, sometimes taking them as lovers. The stories largely paralleled Scottish tales of selkies (see pages 238–239).

Glossary

Aesir In Norse mythology the principal clan of gods, whose ranks included Thor and Odin. A second group was known as the Vanir.

Ahriman The force of evil in the Zoroastrian religion.

amrita In Indian myth, the drink of the gods, conveying immortality on all who sip it.

Annwn The Otherworld of Welsh legend, where the dead and the enchanted enjoyed the pleasures of perpetual youth.

apocalypse A prophetic work revealing wonders. Capitalized, the Apocalypse refers to the biblical Book of Revelation, which describes the ending of the world.

Asgard The home of the gods in Norse myth.

basilicok Chaucer's name for the basilisk, which itself was an intermediate term before the later adoption of "cockatrice".

bestiary Encyclopaedic work describing animal life, produced in manuscript form in the Middle Ages. Bestiaries viewed the beasts they described as elements of God's creation and sought to draw from each one a moral about the divine plan.

Circe Sorceress of classical myth who fell in love with Odysseus but temporarily turned his crew into swine.

cryptozoology The study of animals claimed to exist but currently unknown to science.

Fertile Crescent A crescent-shaped belt of cultivable land stretching northward from the Persian Gulf through Mesopotamia to Syria, then southward down the Mediterranean littoral to the Egyptian border. The Fertile Crescent was home to some of the world's first civilizations.

Grimm Brothers German folklorists whose nineteenth-century compilation of traditional tales became a classic across the Western world.

Hades Also known as Pluto, the lord of the Underworld in classical myth. The name was sometimes applied to the kingdom he ruled over.

Hall of the Two Truths Hall of judgment in ancient Egyptian religion where the god Osiris determined the fate of the souls of the dead.

Hesiod Ancient Greek poet, writing about 700 BCE, whose *Theogony* is a major source for classical creation myths.

kabbalistic Relating to the Kabbalah, the body of Jewish mystical writings concerned with the esoteric interpretation of the Scriptures.

Mahabharata Indian epic, claimed to be the world's longest poem, describing family feuds in the Bharata Dynasty and incorporating important Hindu texts. Its core content dates to the sixth century BCE.

Niflheim Literally "land of mists", the icy realm of the dead in Norse myth, presided over by the goddess Hel, half woman and half corpse.

Olympians The principal gods of classical Greek myth, so called because they resided on top of Mount Olympus.

Physiologus Latin for "naturalist". The purported author of a work that first appeared in Alexandria, Egypt, in the second century CE and that was to serve as a model and source-book for the medieval bestiaries.

Pliny the Elder Prolific Roman author whose encyclopaedic *Natural History*, containing some fabulous as well as much accurate material, was a principal source for scholars for 1,500 years after Pliny's death in the volcanic eruption that destroyed Pompeii in 79 CE.

Prose Edda A key text for Norse mythology, written around the year 1220 by the Icelandic scholar Snorri Sturluson.

Queen Mother of the West In Chinese myth, the ruler of the western paradise and goddess of immortality.

Ragnarok In Norse myth, the battle foretold to occur at the end of the current cycle of existence, which will set the gods, led by Odin, against the forces of chaos unleashed by Loki. Both will be destroyed in the struggle, and a new world will then emerge from the ruins.

Shinto The traditional religion of Japan, involving the worship of nature spirits known as *kami*.

Sumeru Holy mountain that in Buddhist myth was said to be the centre of the world.

Susano Japanese god of the sea and storms, a tempestuous spirit renowned as a divine trouble-maker.

Tartarus The lowest section of the classical Underworld, reserved for those condemned by the gods to eternal punishment.

Valhalla In Norse myth the hall of the god Odin, where he welcomed the souls of warriors killed in battle to a life of perpetual feasting.

Voluspa A poem from the collection of Old Norse works known as the *Poetic Edda* that is the main surviving source for Norse creation myths. Taking the form of a prophetic address by a female seer, it recounts the origins of the world and its eventual end at Ragnarok.

Yellow Emperor Known in Chinese as Huang Di, a legendary early ruler and culture hero who is credited with introducing many of the benefits of civilization to ancient China.

Zoroastrianism The religion of ancient Persia, which saw the world as a battleground between the forces of good and evil. Its sacred text, the *Avesta*, was partly composed by the prophet Zoroaster or Zarathustra.

Further Reading

Aelian (Claudius Aelianus), trans. by A.F. Scholfield. *On the Characteristics of Animals*. Loeb Classical Library, William Heinemann/Harvard University Press: London, 1958.

Baring-Gould, Sabine, ed. by John Matthews. *Myths of the Middle Ages*. Blandford: London, 1996.

Borges, Jorge Luis, trans by Norman Thomas di Giovanni. *The Book of Imaginary Beings*. Penguin: Harmondsworth, Middx, 1974.

Briggs, Katharine M. *An Encyclopedia of Fairies*. Pantheon: New York, 1976.

Briggs, Katharine M. *The Fairies in English Tradition and Literature*. University of Chicago Press: Chicago, 1967.

Briggs, Katharine M. *Pale Hecate's Team*. Routledge: London, 1962.

Burkert, Walter. *Greek Religion*. Harvard University Press: Cambridge, MA, 2001.

Campbell, Joseph (ed.). *The Arabian Nights* [also known as the *1,001 Nights*]. Viking Portable Library: New York, 1952.

Cherry, John (ed.). *Mythical Beasts*. British Museum Press: London, 1995.

Clair, Colin. *Unnatural History: An Illustrated Bestiary*. Abelard-Schuman: London/New York/Toronto, 1967.

Cox, William T. *Fearsome Creatures of the Lumberwoods, with a few Desert and Mountain Beasts*. Bishop Publishing Co.: Sacramento, CA, 1984.

Curtis, Vesta S. *Persian Myths*. British Museum Press: London, 1993.

Davidson, Hilda R. Ellis. *Gods and Myths of Northern Europe*. Penguin: Harmondsworth, Middx, 1964.

Davis, F. Hadland. *Myths and Legends of Japan*. Harrap & Co: London, 1912.

Dallapiccola, Anna L. *Dictionary of Hindu Lore and Legend*. Thames & Hudson: London, 2002.

Ellis, R. *In Search of the Giant Squid*. Penguin: Harmondsworth, Middx, 1999.

English Fairy Tales. Wordsworth Classics: Ware, Herts, 1994.

Gould, R.T. *The Case for the Sea-Serpent*. Philip Allan: London, 1930.

Graves, Robert. *The Greek Myths*. The Folio Society: London, 1996.

Grimm, Jacob & Wilhelm. *The Complete Illustrated Stories of the Brothers Grimm*. Chancellor Press: London, 1985.

Hearn, Lafcadio. *Kwaidan: Stories and Studies of Strange Things*. Tuttle Publishing: Tokyo/Rutland, VT/Singapore, 1971.

Hesiod, trans. by Dorothea Wender. *Theogony*. Penguin: Harmondsworth, Middx, 1976.

Heuvelmans, Bernard, trans. by Richard Garnett. *On the Track of Unknown Animals*. Hill & Wang: New York, 1958.

Heuvelmans, Bernard, trans. by Richard Garnett. *In the Wake of the Sea Serpent*. Hill & Wang: New York, 1968.

Howatson, M.C. *The Oxford Companion to Classical Literature*. Oxford University Press: Oxford, 1989.

Jarvie, Gordon (ed.). *Scottish Folk and Fairy Tales*. Penguin: Harmondsworth, Middx, 1997.

Jones, Gwyn. *Welsh Legends and Folk Tales*. Puffin Classics: Harmondsworth, Middx, 1970.

Leach, Maria, and Fried, Jerome (ed.). *Funk & Wagnall's Standard Dictionary of Folklore, Mythology, and Legend*. HarperCollins: San Francisco, 1984.

Littleton, C. Scott (ed.). *Mythology: The Illustrated Anthology of World Myth and Storytelling*. Duncan Baird Publishers: London, 2002.

Mack, Carol K. and Dinah. *A Field Guide to Demons, Fairies, Fallen Angels and Other Subversive Spirits*. Arcade Publishing: New York, 1998.

Matthews, John and Caitlin. *The Element Encyclopedia of Magical Creatures*. HarperElement: London, 2005.

Metzger, Bruce M., and Coogan, Michael D. *The Oxford Companion to the Bible*. Oxford University Press: Oxford, 1993.

Miller, Mary, and Taube, Karl. *The Gods and Symbols of Ancient Mexico and the Maya*. Thames & Hudson: London, 1993.

Orbell, Margaret. *The Illustrated Encyclopedia of Maori Myth and Legend*. Canterbury University Press: Christchurch, NZ, 1995.

Payne, Ann. *Medieval Beasts*. New Amsterdam Books: New York, 1990.

The Physiologus, trans. & ed. by Francis J. Carmody. Book Club of California: San Francisco, 1953.

Pickering, David. *Cassell Dictionary of Superstitions*. Cassell: London, 1995.

Pliny the Elder, trans. & ed. by John Healy. *Natural History: A Selection*. Penguin: Harmondsworth, Middx, 1991.

Polo, Marco, trans. & ed. by Ronald Latham. *The Travels of Marco Polo*. The Folio Society: London, 1968.

Rose, Carol. *Giants, Monsters and Dragons: An Encyclopedia of Folklore, Legend and Myth*. Norton: New York, 2000.

Scott, Sir Walter. *Letters on Demonology and Witchcraft*. S.R. Publishing: Wakefield, Yorks, 1968.

Shuker, Karl. *Dragons: A Natural History*. Barnes & Noble: New York, 2003.

Tolkien, J.R.R. *The Lord of the Rings*. George Allen & Unwin: London, 1955.

White, T.H. *The Book of Beasts*. Jonathan Cape: London, 1954.

Yeats, W.B. (ed.). *Fairy and Folk Tales of Ireland*. Picador, London, 1979.

249

Index

253

Acknowledgments

Picture Credits

The publisher would like to thank the following people, museums and photographic libraries for permission to reproduce their material. Every care has been taken to trace copyright holders. However, if we have omitted anyone we apologize and will, if informed, make corrections to any future edition.

Page 29 Hercules and the Stymphalian birds. Engraving from a Greek vase (Bibliothèque des Arts Décoratifs, Paris/Dagli Orti/The Art Archive)

31 The simurgh leads an army of birds. Miniature from a 17th-century Persian manuscript *Anvar-i Suhayli*, a version of the *Kalila wa Dimna* fables (British Library, London. Add. 18579, f.104)

34 *Virgil, Dante and the Erinyes or Furies* by Gustave Doré, from *The Divine Comedy* by Dante Alighieri. Engraving, 1885, Paris (Bibliothèque des Arts Décoratifs, Paris/The Bridgeman Art Library)

111 Manuscript illustration by the Boucicaut Master (fl.1390-1430), showing wolf-headed people of the Andaman Islands (Bibliothèque Nationale, Paris. Ms Fr 2810/The Bridgeman Art Library)

115 Illustration from the *Ashmole Bestiary* of a bonnacon showing his contempt for the attacking knights. England, early thirteenth century (Bodleian Library, Oxford, Ashmole 1511 f. 18r./The Art Archive)

129 Miniature illustration from the *Bhagavata-Purana* showing the Apparition of Varaha. India, Pahari School, ca. 1730 (Chandigarh Museum/Jean-Louis Nou/akg-images)

133 The Ewaiponoma or Blemmyae, from the account of Raleigh's search for El Dorado, Collection of Voyages, *Kurtze wunderbare Beschreibung des Goldreichen Konigreichs Guianae in America* by Levinus Hulsius. Published in Nuremberg, 1599 (British Library, London. C.114.c.15, plate XV)

134 A sciapod. Engraving from *Registrum Hujus Operis Libri … by* Hartmannus Schedel. Published by Anton Koberger, Nuremberg, 1493 (British Library, London. IC.7452)

140–141 A *Satyr mourning over a Nymph* by Piero di Cosimo, ca. 1495. Oil on panel (The National Gallery, London/The Bridgeman Art Library)

153 Cat-woman monster. Engraving from J.W. Schmuck's *Fasculi*, 1679 (Fortean Picture Library)

171 *Gnomes mourn their Princess* by Alfred Zimmermann, 1903. From *Jugend* periodical, Germany (Bibliothèque des Arts Décoratifs, Paris/Dagli Orti/The Art Archive)

181 *The Nightmare* by Henry Fuseli, 1781. Oil on canvas (The Detroit Institute of Arts, Founders Society purchase with Mr and Mrs Bert L. Smokler/The Bridgeman Art Library)

187 Artist's depiction of an Almas, based on eyewitness descriptions (Richard Svensson/Fortean Picture Library)

214 A possible sighting of the Loch Ness Monster, 1934. Photograph (Keystone/Hulton Archive/Getty Images)

230 Detail of a Chinese Qing Dynasty (1633–1912) Kesi dragon robe. Embroidered silk (Private Collection, Photo © Bonhams, London/The Bridgeman Art Library)

231 Detail of the ceramic "Nine Dragon Screen", Forbidden City, Beijing (TravelInk/Robert Harding World Imagery)

Commissioned Artworks

Tomislav Tomic: pages 1, 23, 49, 53, 63, 64, 67, 72, 79, 82, 83, 92, 106, 119, 127, 138, 143, 145, 147, 149, 157, 159, 162, 169, 175, 177, 182, 185, 189, 204, 211, 236, 242, 244, 245, 246, 247

Peter Visscher: pages 4–5 (detail of cockatrice, page 25), 9, 12, 19, 25, 41, 47, 59, 91, 97, 117, 137, 193, 197, 201, 207, 213, 219, 227, 239, 241

Garry Walton: pages 2, 6–7 (detail of longwang, page 229), 11, 13, 14–15 (detail of thunderbird, page 17), 17, 21, 27, 33, 37, 39, 43, 51, 54–55, 57, 69, 77, 80–81, 85, 89, 101, 105, 108–109, 123, 130–131, 155, 164–165, 166, 173, 179, 191, 198–199, 217, 220–221, 225, 229

Additional artworks by Gary A. Lippincott (page 113) and Stephen Player (page 121)